FROM THE "KING OF THE REBUS"

Norman Blumenthal has the distinction of being the Producer of the longest continually running Game Show in the history of television. NBC-TV's CONCENTRATION (with Norm as the brains behind the scenes) ran for over fourteen and a half years. He also created every single one of the more than 8,000 "rebus" puzzles used on the show. Thus, his humble claim to the title "King of the Rebus."

In this challenging new book, Norm brings you a brand-new twist on those very popular rebus forms—SCRAMBLE. SCRAMBLE will challenge you, amuse you, anger and frustrate you—and bring you hours of intellectually stimulating fun.

SCRAMBLE

the PICTURE PUZZLES that
make you stop and think.

Norman Blumenthal

Other books by Norman Blumenthal

THE TV GAMES SHOWS: How to Get on and Win

PYRAMID BOOKS ▲ NEW YORK

For
Howie, Bobby, Lori
and Sylvia
with love

SCRAMBLE: A PYRAMID BOOK

Pyramid edition published July 1976

Library of Congress Catalog Card Number: 76-19219

Printed in the United States of America

Pyramid Books are published by Pyramid Publications (Harcourt Brace Jovanovich). Its trademarks, consisting of the word "Pyramid" and the portrayal of a pyramid, are registered in the United States Patent Office.

PYRAMID PUBLICATIONS
(Harcourt Brace Jovanovich)
757 Third Avenue, New York, N.Y. 10017

Layout and Production by Anthony Basile
Graphic Design by Norman Blumenthal

(Introduction)

This is the first edition of a new brain-twister game called *Scramble*. It will challenge you, amuse you, make you angry, frustrate you—but I guarantee that *Scramble* will prove to be an intellectually stimulating pastime. Everybody loves to solve puzzles, so get your pencils sharpened, make sure you have an eraser handy and I'll explain how *Scramble* works.

Scramble is a brand-new twist on a very old and popular puzzle form—the *rebus*. A rebus can either be a well-known phrase, the title of something, or a famous person's name which is broken down into a series of sound-components. These components are depicted visually by pictures of objects, by letters and parts of words cleverly arranged to confuse and amuse the reader.

For example, the word *rebus* would be portrayed by the syllable *re* connected to a picture of a bus by means of a plus sign.

re+

The word *scramble* would be depicted as follows:

Although I did not invent this puzzle form, I might humbly claim the dubious title of "king of the rebus," because I probably conceived more of these puzzles than any man in history. Aside from the hundreds I originated while working as a commercial artist for various publications and children's books. I concocted every one of the more than eight thousand puzzles used on the longest continually running network game show in TV history—"Concentration." This is exclusive of the more than two thousand I created for the home version game sold in toy stores. During the fifteen years that I produced this network game show, I was faced with an everpresent problem: keeping one step ahead of the contestants. Whenever I felt they were solving my puzzles too quickly, I was obliged to make them tougher by adding more remote clues and taking more liberties with the English language. Over the years I've bent, stretched and literally mutilated word sounds to suit my own evil purposes; I've employed every weird word-breakup, dialect, pun and trick I could think of to keep my puzzles challenging. But never, in any of my attempts to contort and distort our language, did I ever include anything that might've been considered unfair or offensive. I feel I've succeeded when some of my more bizarre creations evoke a smile and a gentle "Aren't you terrible" when solved. I refer to my methods as "taking liberties" or, if you will, "poetic license." So I guess that's not really so terrible, as long as we both have fun. You, in solving them—and me, in making them up. I must've been doing something right; my puzzles, as well as the TV program, kept the viewers entertained long enough to make "Concentration" one of the most popular game shows ever.

As I said earlier, I did not invent the rebus, I simply borrowed it from the past, modernized it, and made it popular again with millions of people in many parts of the world. Where did it begin? Who actually drew the first rebus? I'm afraid the reference books I've pored through cannot give us that information. Perhaps the credit belongs to pre-historic man who left cave drawings, which could be considered puzzles or messages, so we could better understand his way of life. American Indians painted pictures and symbols on their teepees to depict stories of great buffalo hunts and other heroic and historic events.

Through the centuries, the rebus was used with increasing frequency on coats of arms, trademarks, hallmarks, tavern and inn signs, and even on the branding irons of modern ranches. Benjamin Franklin used the rebus in many of his publications, including *Poor Richard's Almanac*, to teach us adages to live by. "*A PEN + KNEE SAFE + 'D IS A PEN + KNEE URN + 'D*" was one of the many he included. Forgive me, Ben, I used my own method—you would've used plus and minus signs in your day. I prefer the method I employed on my show and in this book: plus signs only.

I realize that many of you know how to solve these puzzles, but for the unindoctrinated, here are some of the finer points of rebus solving.

You already know that whenever a plus sign appears after an element or symbol, it has to be connected to the very next element. This will create a complete word, as in *re* + *bus*. However, in many instances, I'll create two complete words in this manner, as in *an* + *tie*, which means *and I*. (I warned you about how tricky I can be.) By the way, one picture can represent more than one word. A picture of the tropical bird, the *toucan*, might start the phrase: "Two can play the same game."

With regard to single letters, they are used in three different ways. *M* + *eye* means *my;* if that same letter M is preceded by an apostrophe, the sound is softened, as in *mmm*. Therefore, *eye* + *'m* would be *I'm;* if there are quotation marks around a letter, the actual sound of the letter is important, as in *"M"* + *tea*, which translates into the word *empty*.

Similarly, all numerals are pronounced the way they sound as in *4* + *get*, which represents *forget*, and almost pronounced the way they sound—whenever I take liberties—as in *2* + *wing* to mean *doing*.

Drawings of objects such as bottles with labels reading gin, ale, rye, rum, etc. stand for gin, ale, rye, rum, etc. If the bottle has no label, it stands for the word *bottle*. A can of lye + 't would stand for the word *light*.

Drawings containing accent lines such as a human leg with the knee accented stand for *knee*, not *leg;* accent lines around the point of a pencil signify *point*, not *pencil*.

If you see a picture of a book, don't get too technical; it is not a manual, a novel, a tome, or anything else—it's simply a book. A picture of a bell is a bell, not a ring (just because it does). Please don't complicate my puzzles any more than I have. They are difficult enough. Simply sound out the elements over and over, and eventually they will make cents—sorry, I mean sense. You may not believe this is true, but I actually think and write in rebus. Since I started making up this type of puzzle—M + ICE + BELL + INK HAS PIN OFF + EGG + TED—my spelling has been affected.

Now that you understand how to work out my rebus puzzles, and because I want to stay 'one step ahead of you', I've invented a more sophisticated puzzle game, which I call SCRAMBLE. Here's how it works:

Each *Scramble* set consists of three rebus puzzles for you to solve, and a fourth puzzle for you to construct by filling in the blanks. The necessary elements are underlined in the first three puzzles and must be arranged properly to form the fourth puzzle.

EXAMPLE: ___

Puzzle 1: EYE TH + INK U R DOVE + EYE + 'N
Solution: "I THINK YOU ARE DIVINE"
Puzzle 2: BEE + 10 TOOTH + UH PUNCH
Solution: "BEATEN TO THE PUNCH"
Puzzle 3: BIRD P + ARK + 'S
Solution: "BERT PARKS"

In these puzzles, the underlined elements are: *dove*, *bee*, *10*, *bird* and *'s*. By trying them in different order, or sequence, they will spell out the phrase which is the fourth puzzle. The general category or some other hint is provided.

Puzzle 4: HELPFUL ANIMAL
BEE + 'S + DOVE BIRD + 10
Solution: "BEAST OF BURDEN"

Below each fourth puzzle there is a work area for you to write in as you try to un*Scramble* the elements for the proper sequence and answer.

The puzzles at the beginning of this book are easy, but they will get progressively more difficult, as you become progressively more proficient at *Scramble*. The answers appear at the back of the book. As a puzzle fancier, myself, I'm always disappointed when I look for the answer to a question, or the solution to a problem that has me stumped. Very often, my eyes accidentally pick up the solution to the next puzzle, and it spoils my fun. Crusader that I am, I decided that my book would be different.

I separated the list of answers into two sections—odd and even numbers. Also, to give you a second chance at a puzzle you can't work out, I'm including a phonetic list (the elements spelled out in words), and if you still can't figure it out, a conventional answer list. Even if you have difficulty, don't peek. Keep on trying, and you'll work it out.

Enjoy this book. See how adept you become at *Scramble* as you progress from easy to difficult. As soon as you finish this book, be on the lookout for more brain teasers in *Scramble* volumes to follow.

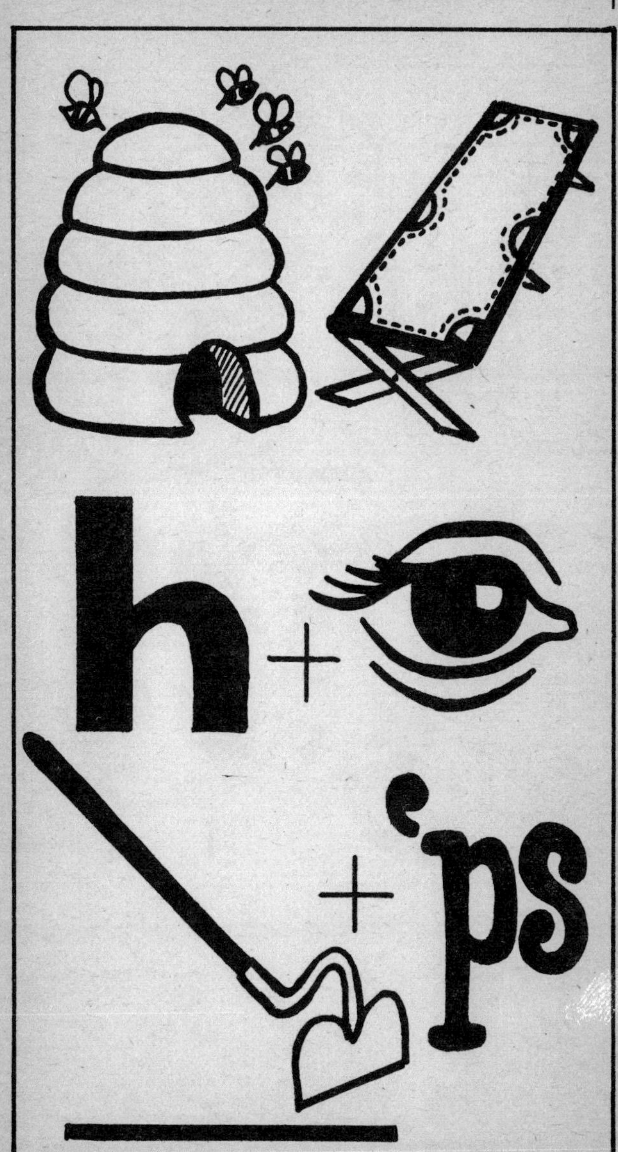
h +
+ 'ps

YUV
GUM
2
THE
RYE
+ 't
PL +
A
A

a
inn
+
4
+
'md
+

4. GREETING

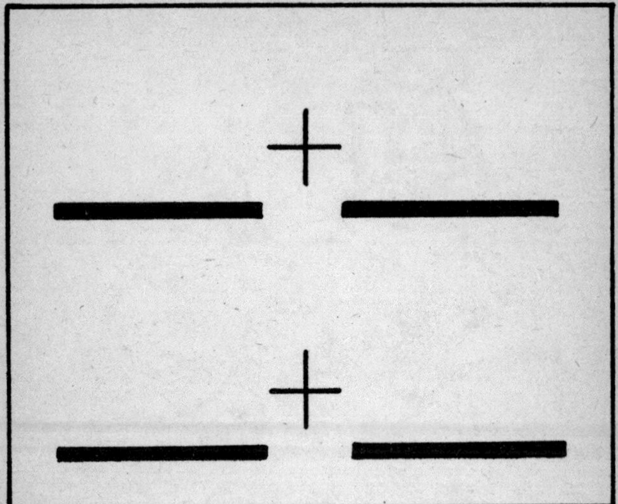

WORK AREA:

F + 8TH + O +
+ 80

"N"
+
OFF
ALE
+
OWN

HOO
WH+
air
WH+

8. EARLY AMERICAN

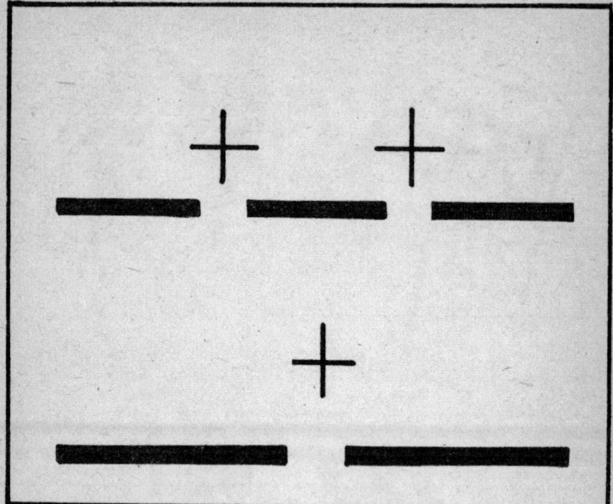

WORK AREA:

DEED
U
C
TH
+

a

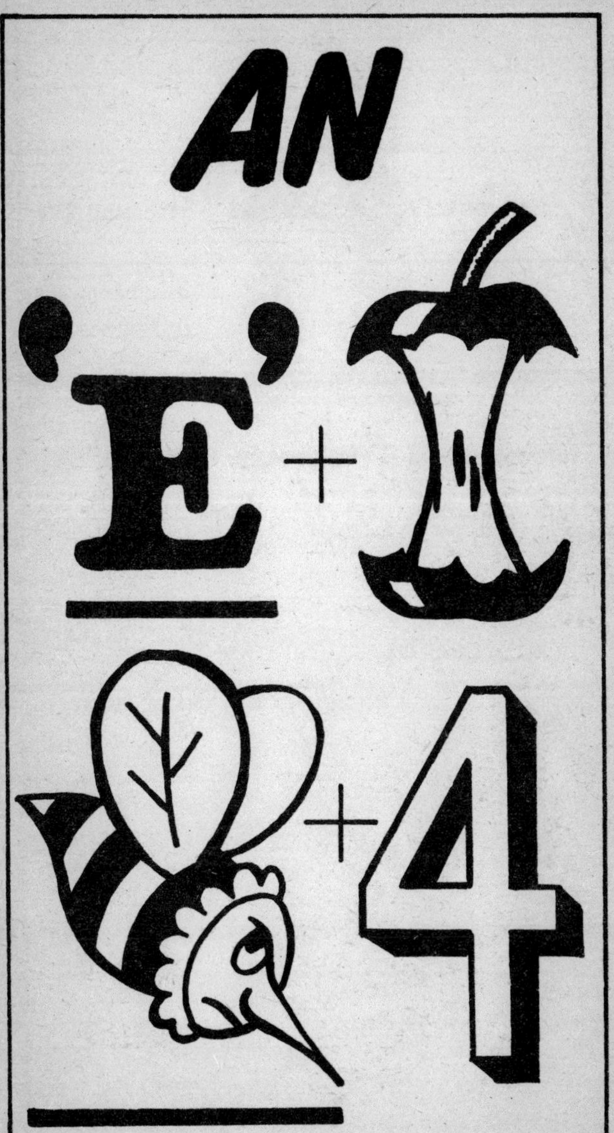
AN
'E'
+
+
4

12. VERY SIMPLE

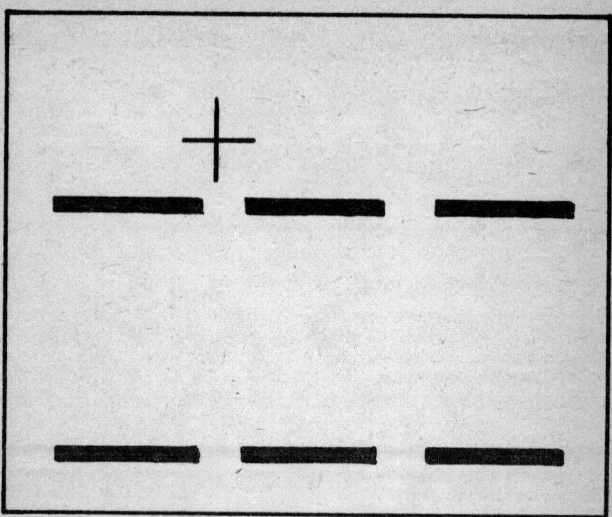

WORK AREA:

'C' +
S +
inn + 'D' + inn

ON
THE
CIDER
THE
S
'
t

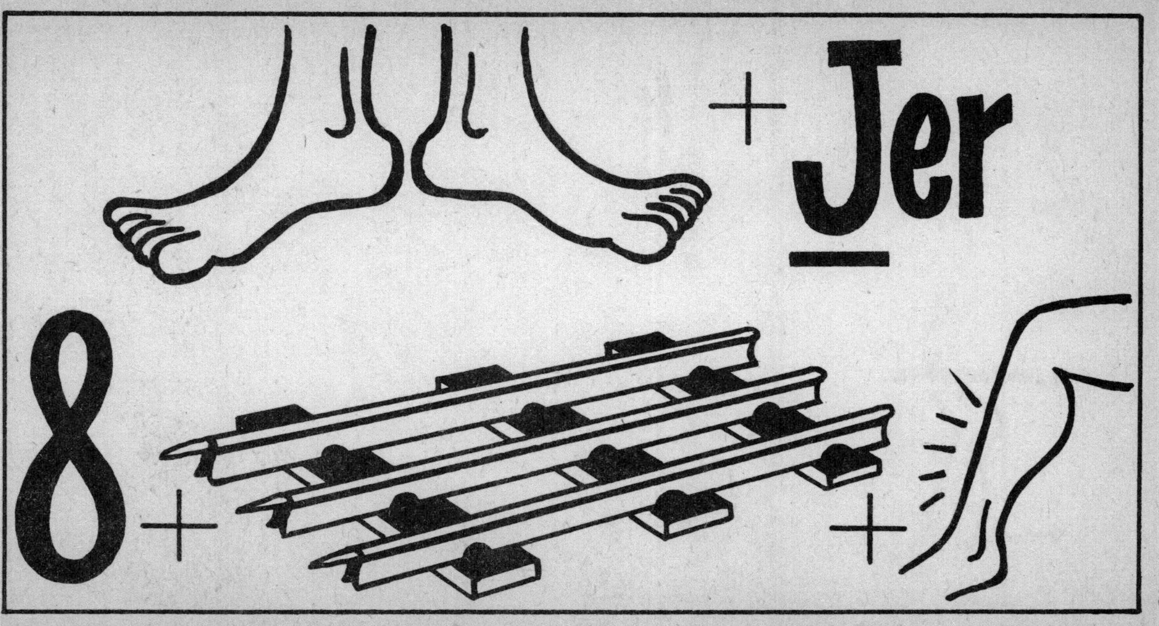
Jer
8

16. MR. ED'S BOSS

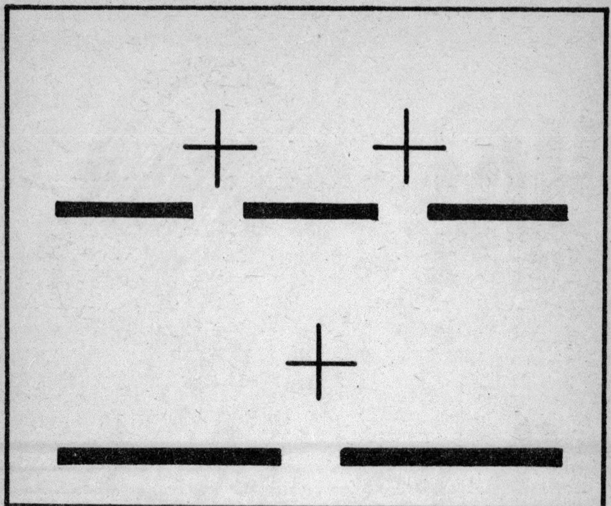

WORK AREA:

WH +
+ in

B
+
ale
+
UH
+
+
GO
+

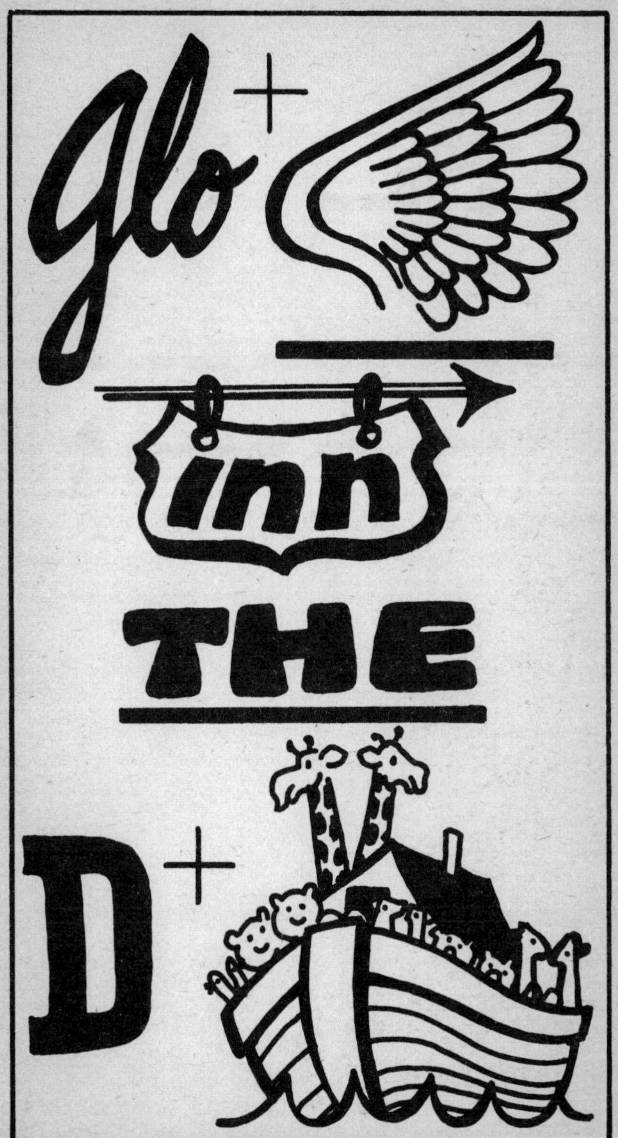
glo +
inn
THE
D +

20. TAKEN LITERALLY

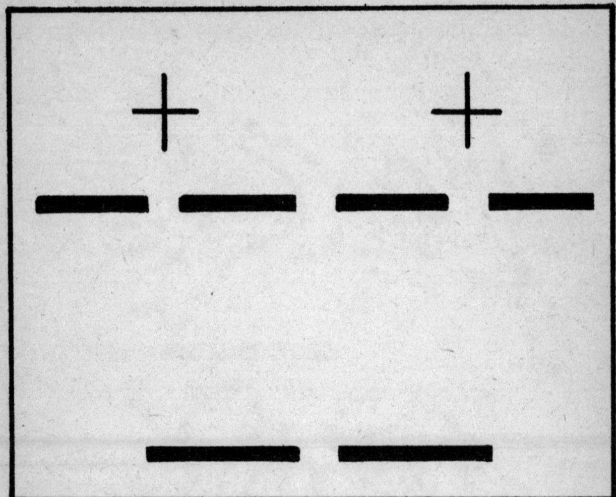

WORK AREA:

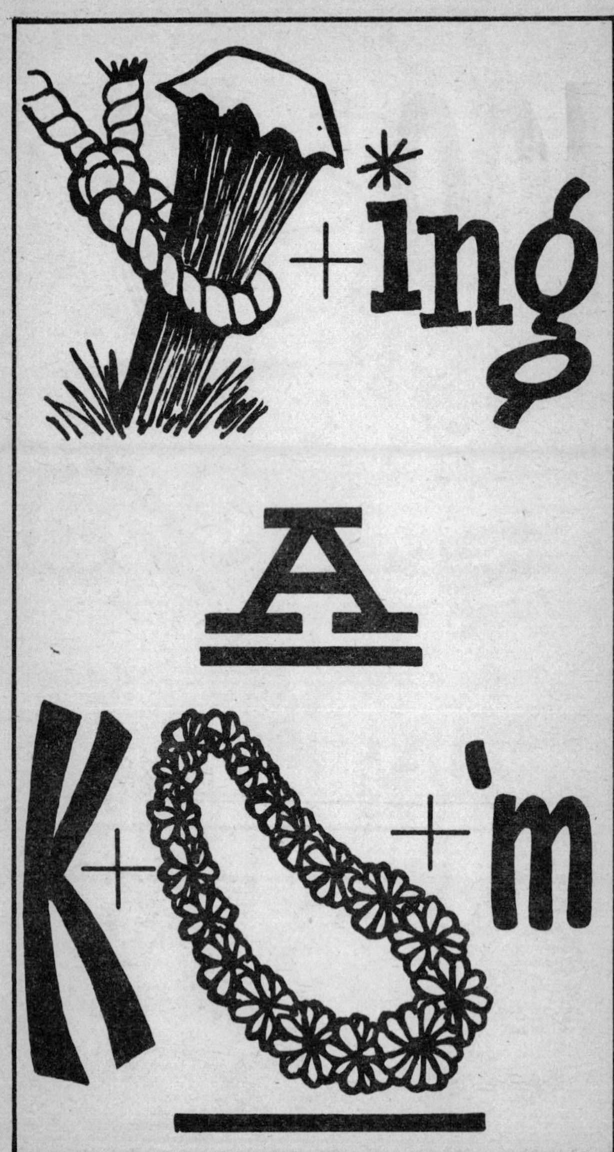
+ ing
A
K +
+ 'm

LOO +
a
B +
+ er

24. SHORTCUT

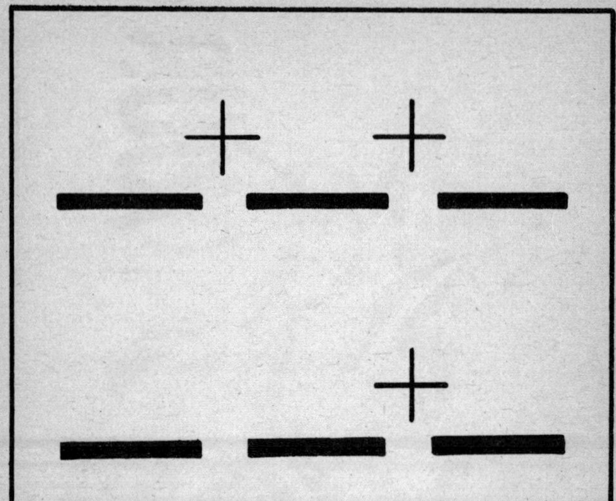

WORK AREA:

DUH +
+ 'S + + YOUR

RUM
THE

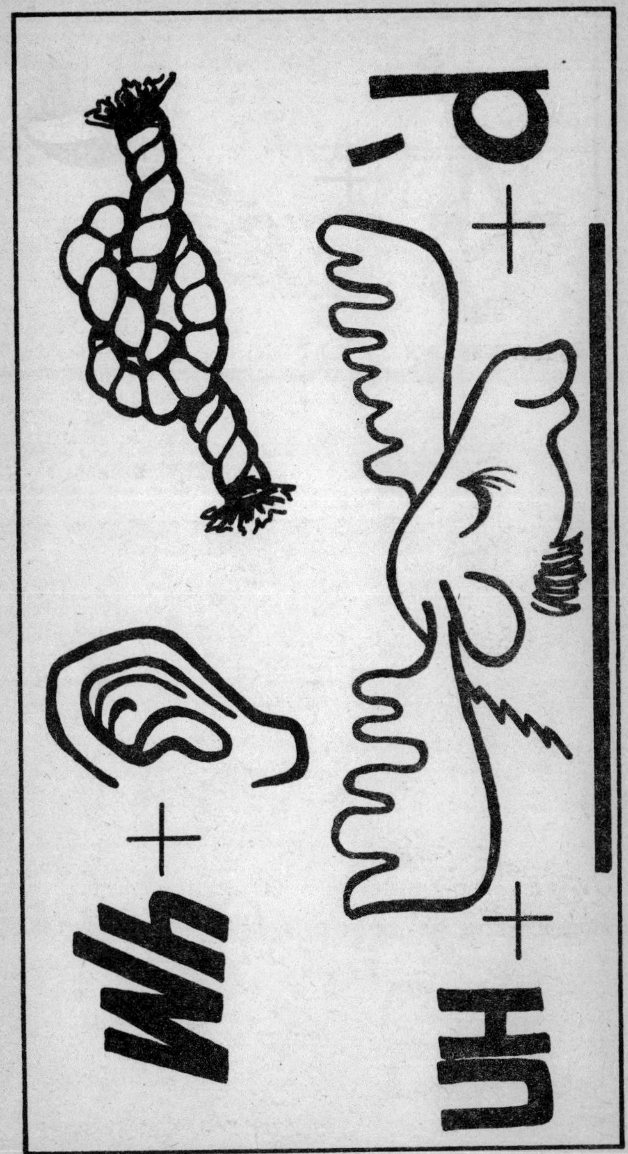

28. OLD TV SHOW

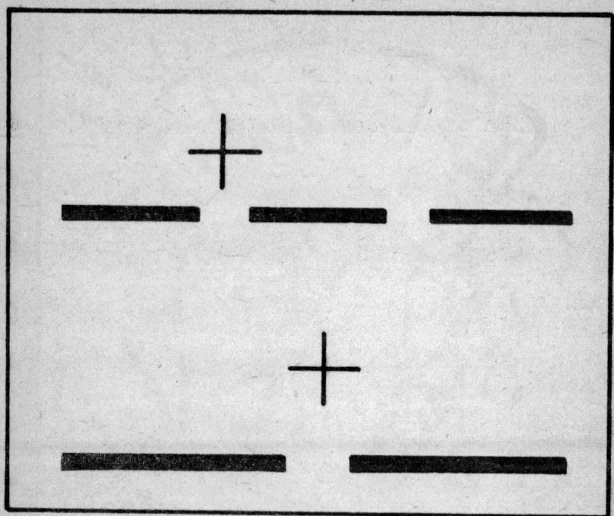

WORK AREA:

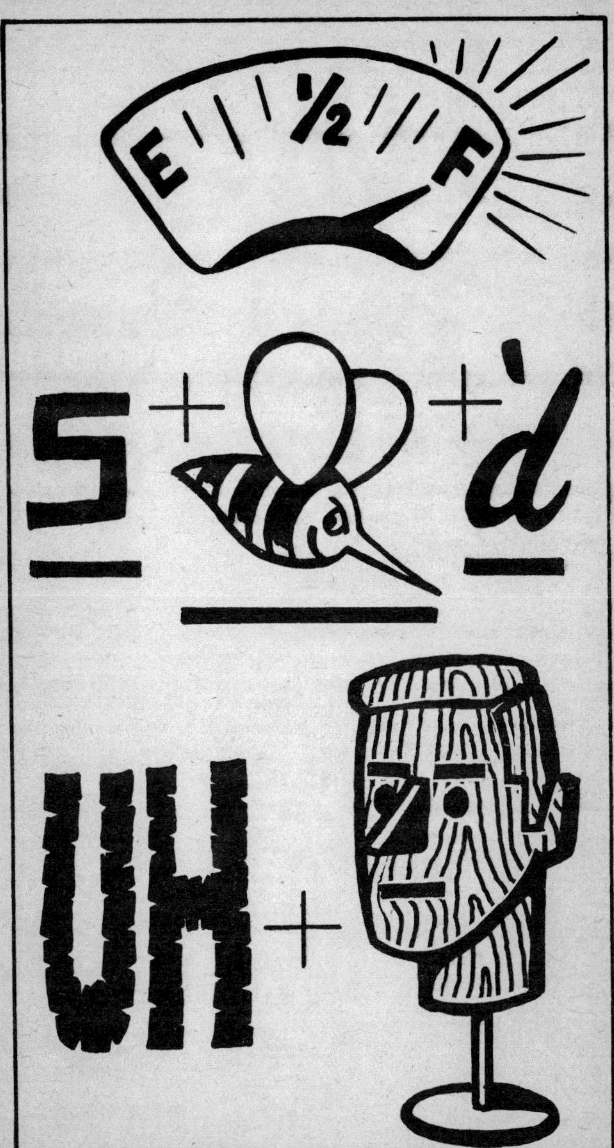
E
½
F
S
+
+
'd
UH
+

YORE

GO
2
A
NEW
+
+
er

32. OLD DELI FAVORITE

WORK AREA:

'NT
F
LYE
OFF
THE

8
+
+
OAK
S
+

AH
TRICK

36. ON ROCKY GROUND

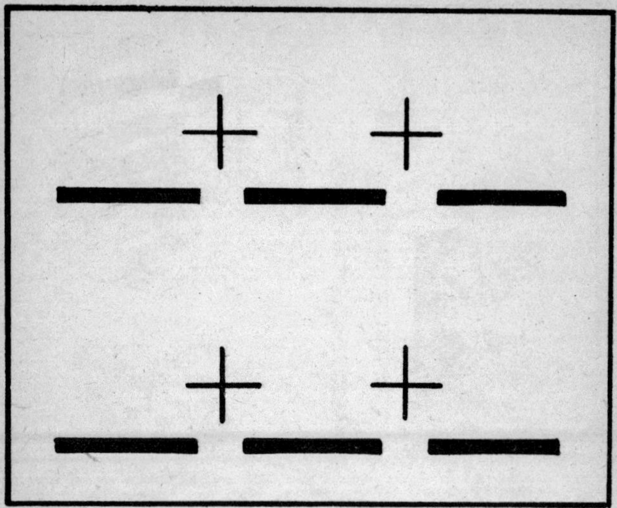

WORK AREA:

+ E
+
+ YOU'D

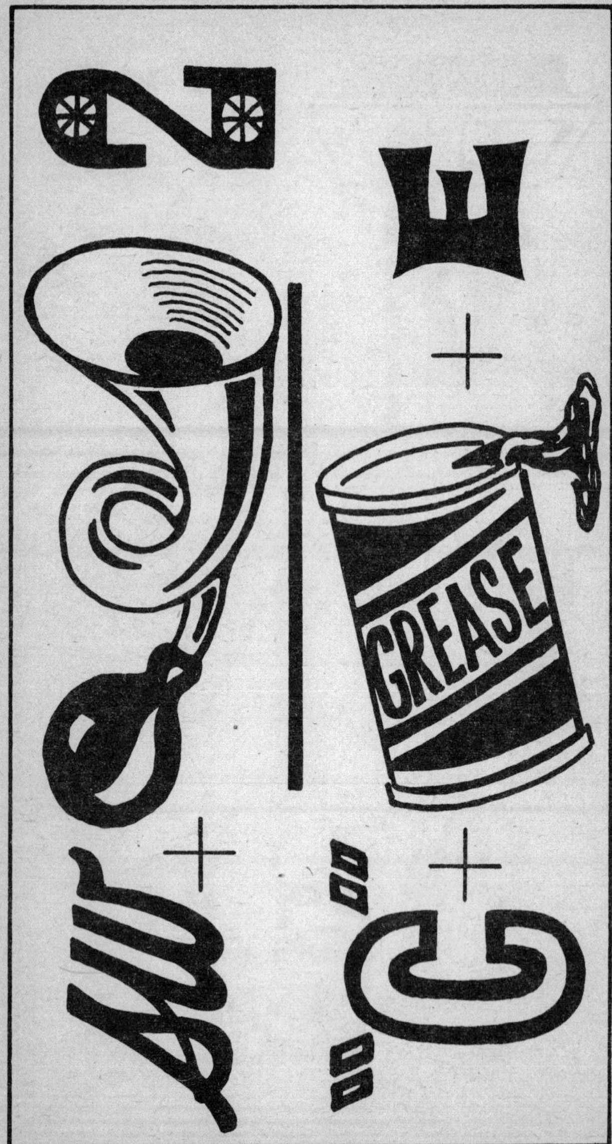
GREASE

sh
COO
'K

40. OVERSEAS BOND

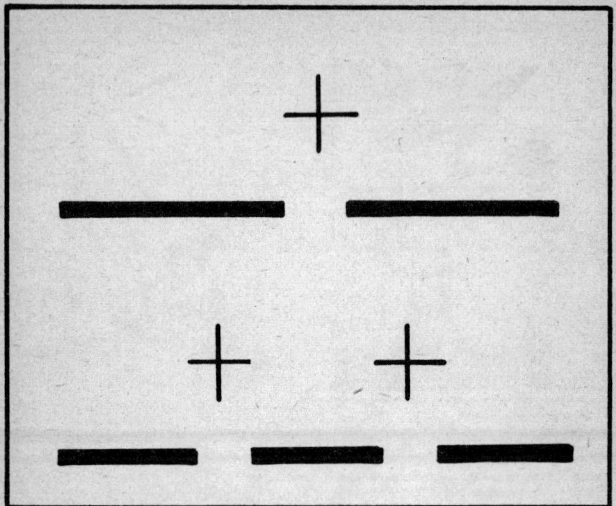

WORK AREA:

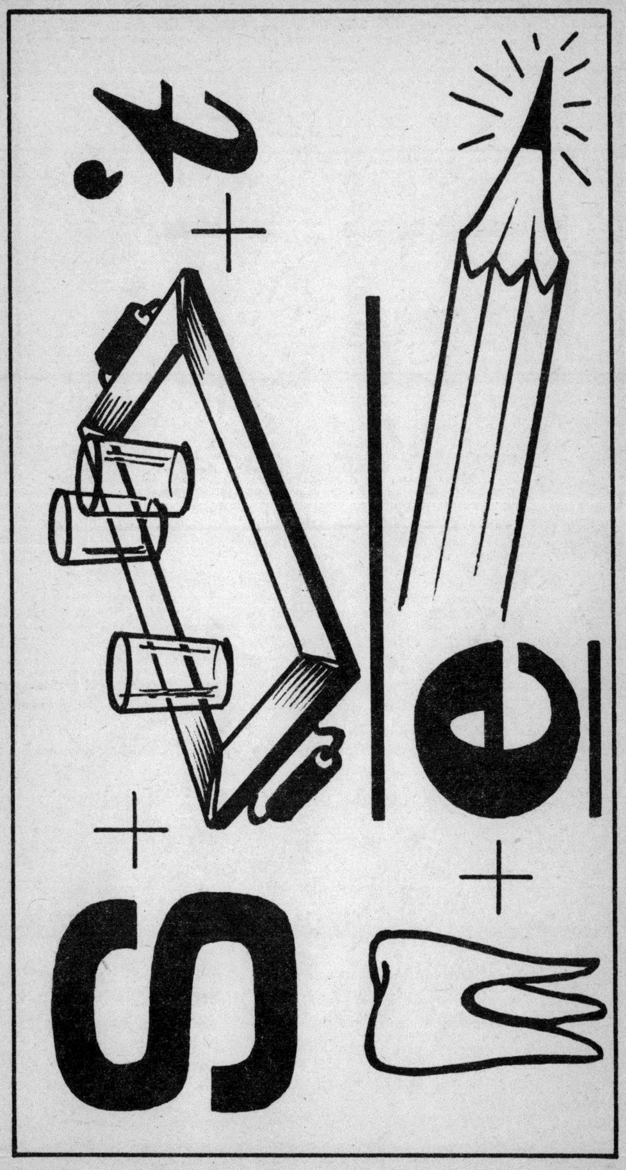

L
RAH

THEE

44. WESTWARD HO!

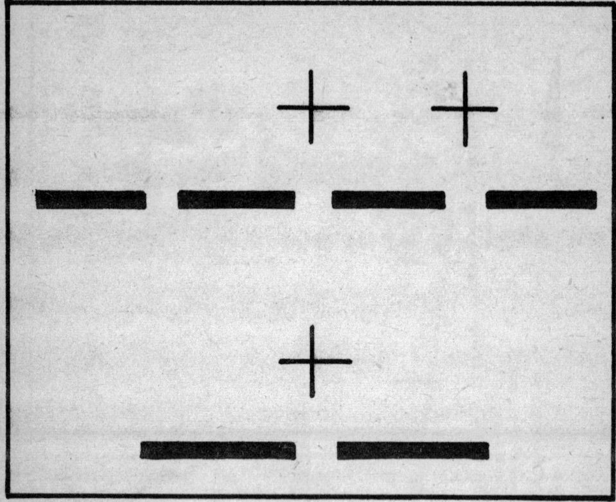

WORK AREA:

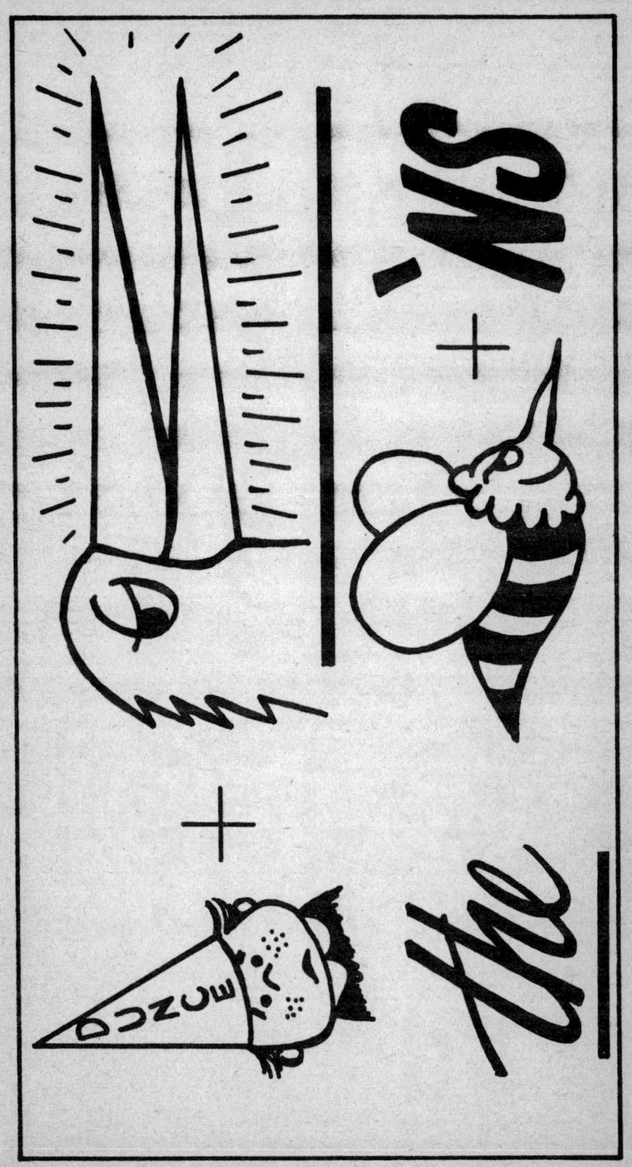
'NS
the
DUNCE

a
+
TAZ
+
+

anne

IN

48. RASH RUSSIAN

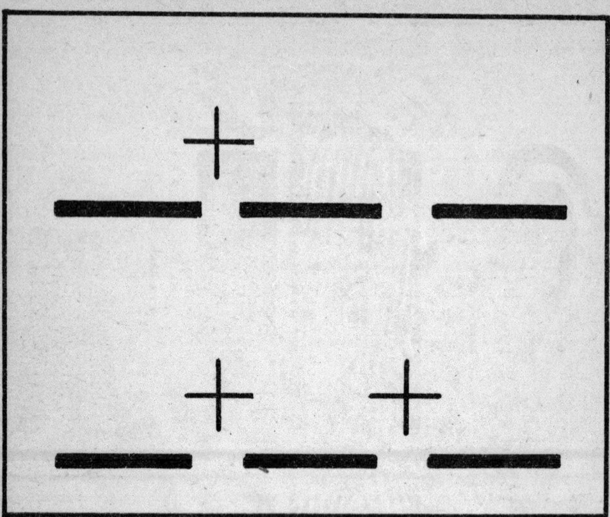

WORK AREA:

T
AS a
d
RUM

+ er
U
Th +
ME

52. PILLOW TALK

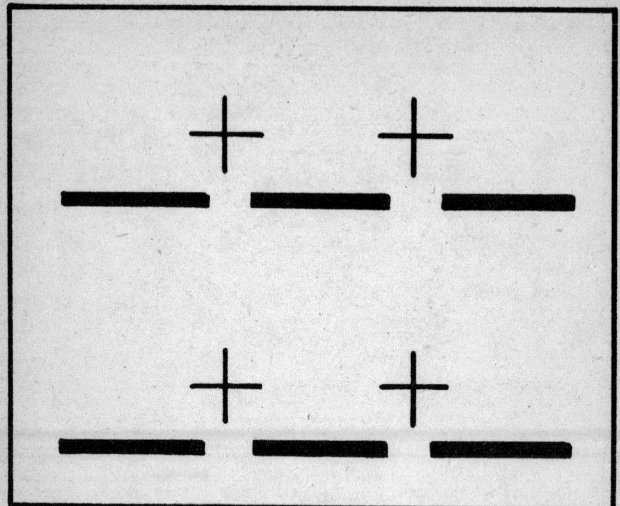

WORK AREA:

RICE
2
THE

its
1
OF
th +
D +
A
A

an AP + 4

the T +

56. BONUS BUY

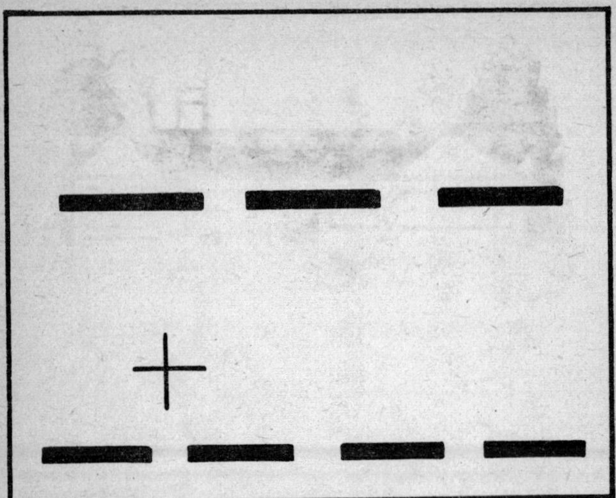

WORK AREA:

TH
+
UGH
+

A
+
SALT
&
+

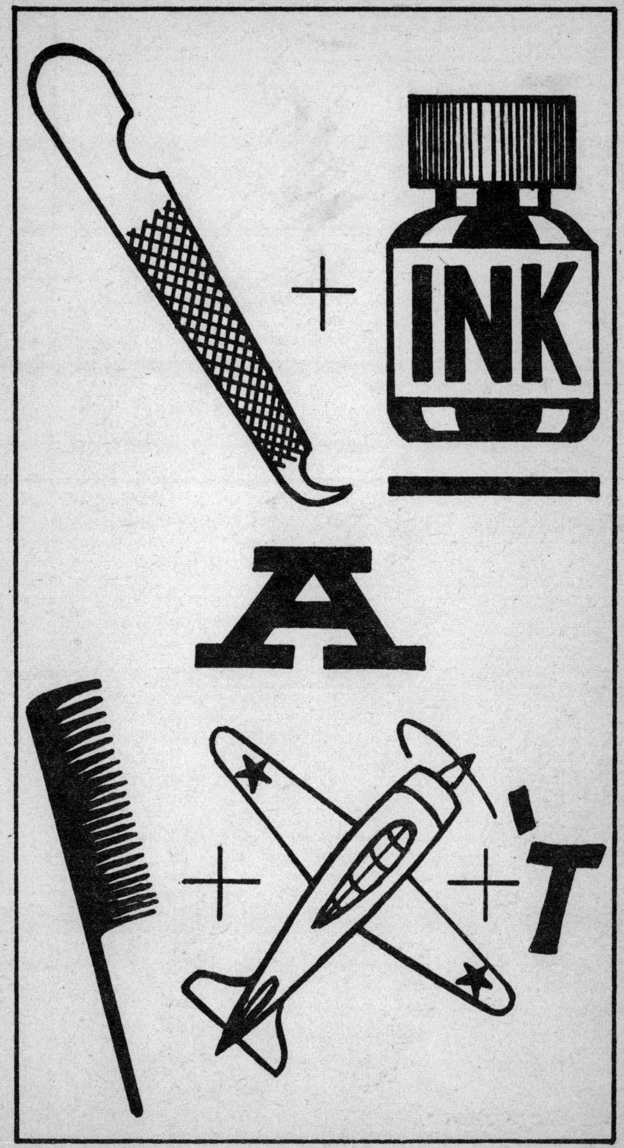
INK
A
'T

60. PERFECT SCORE

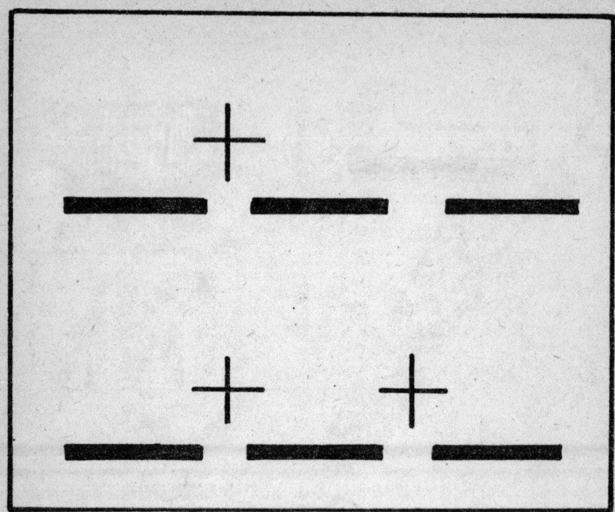

WORK AREA:

THE
EAT
L
T
RYE

'P
UN
UH
4

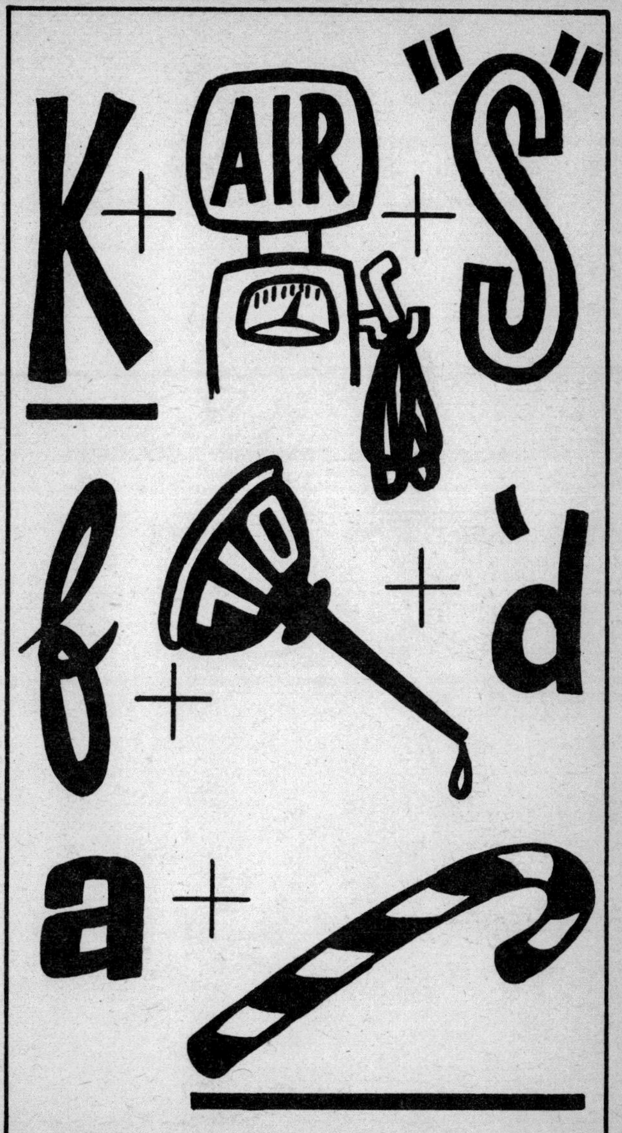
K
AIR
"S"
OIL
'd
a

64. DIXIE DIGNITARY

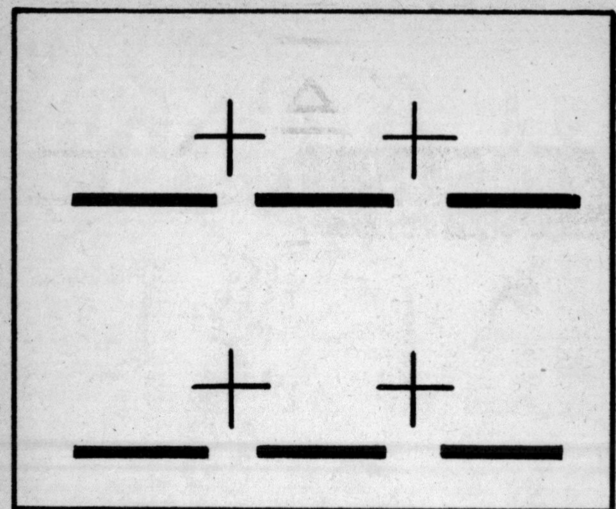

WORK AREA:

A
mo +
MAY +
'm
+

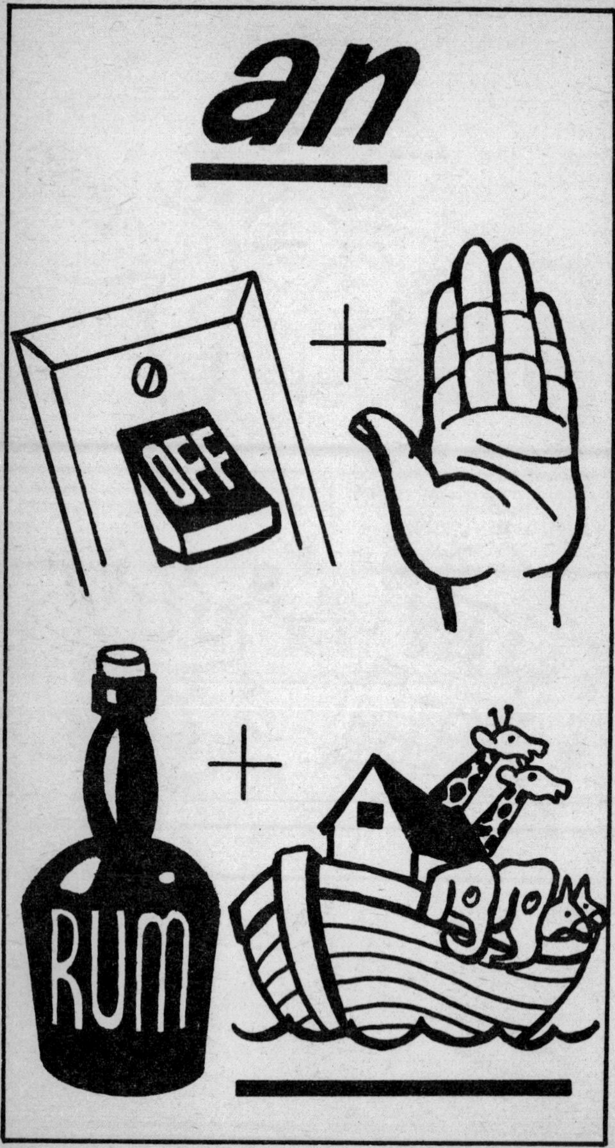
an
OFF
RUM

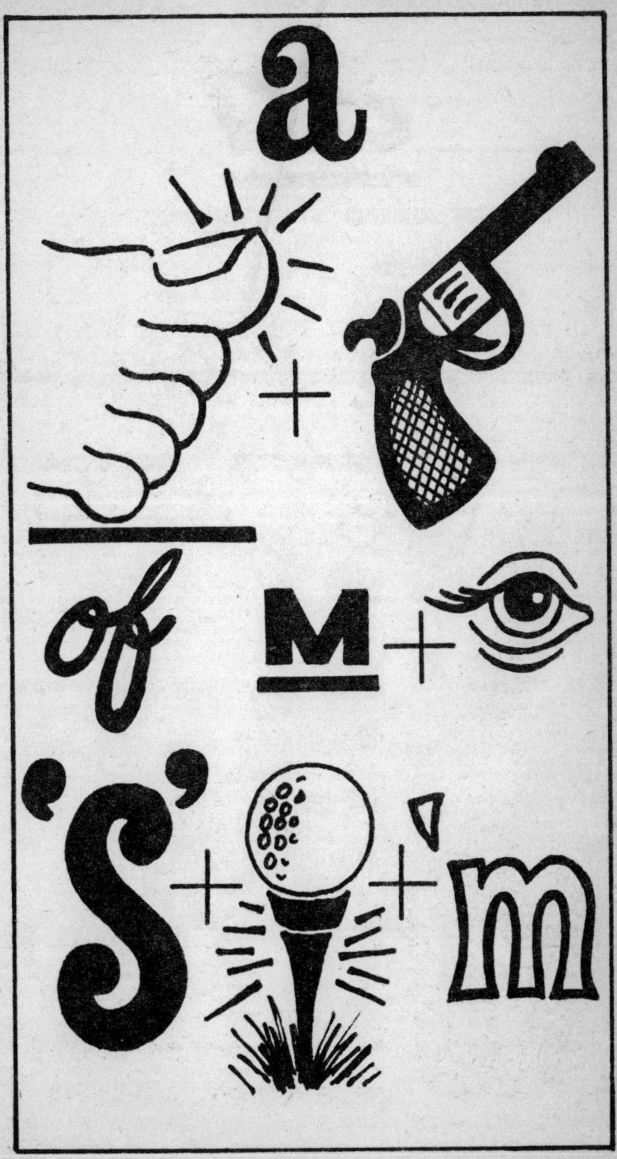
a
+
of
M
+
'S'
+
+
'm

68. EMPIRE STATESMAN

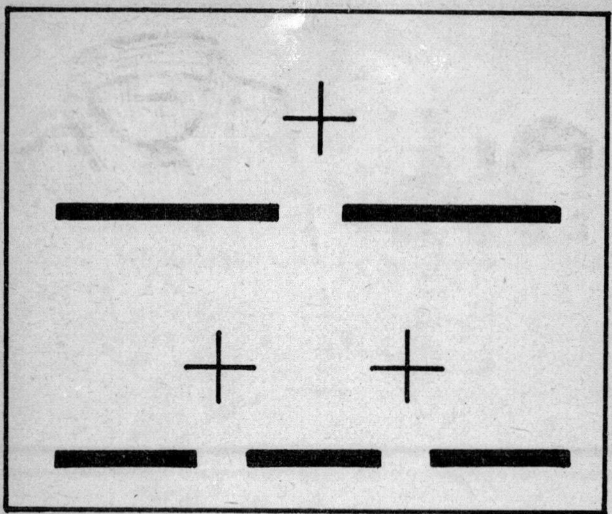

WORK AREA:

Rit
+
+
2000

N
THE
f
d

Tra
+
+

72. RIVERBOAT

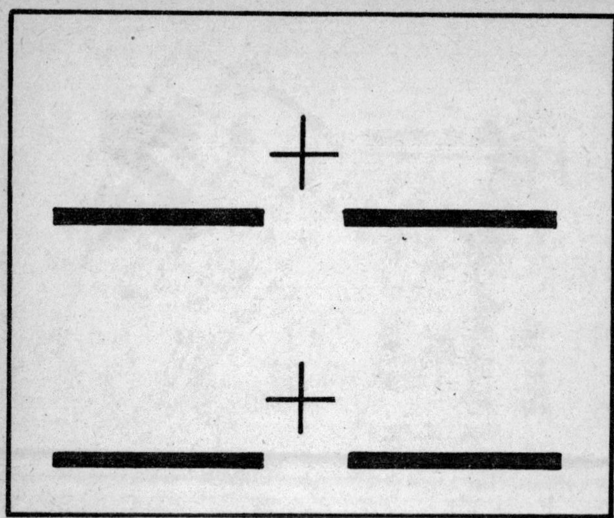

WORK AREA:

TELLER
'N'

LYE
EVIL

'm
A
ing

76. NOTHING BUT THE TRUTH

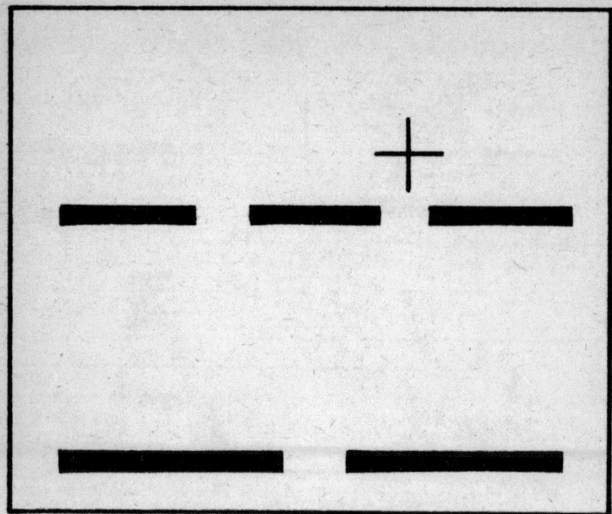

WORK AREA:

TAY
+
ah
+

inn
A
+ ER
of
S +
+ ing

STR
UGH
L
4
5
L

80. A GOOD START

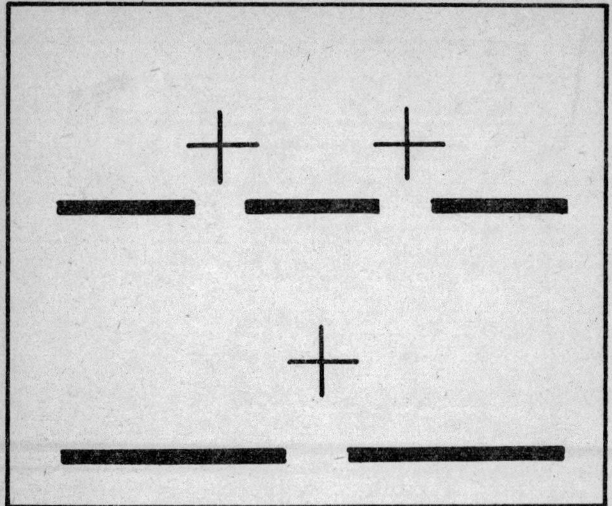

WORK AREA:

SEED + + A +
KA + + E

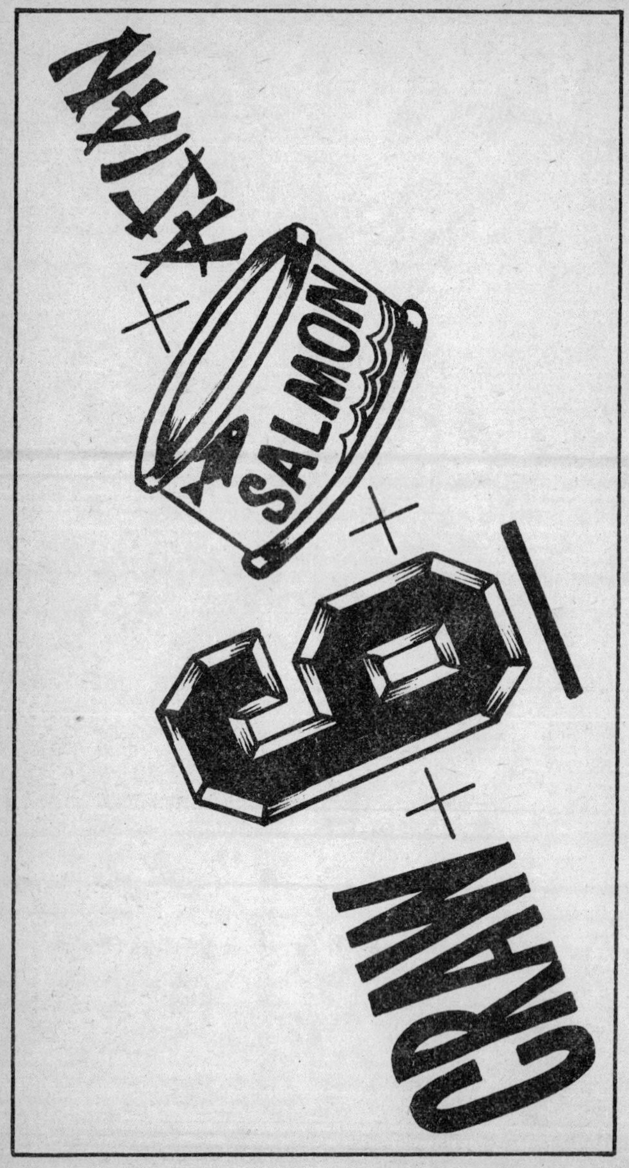
ASIAN
SALMON
5
CRAB

LEE
INK
LYE
'ND

84. YEARBOOK CAPTION

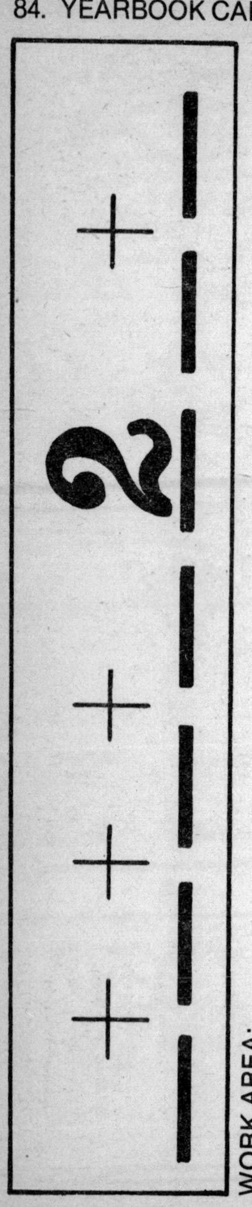

WORK AREA:

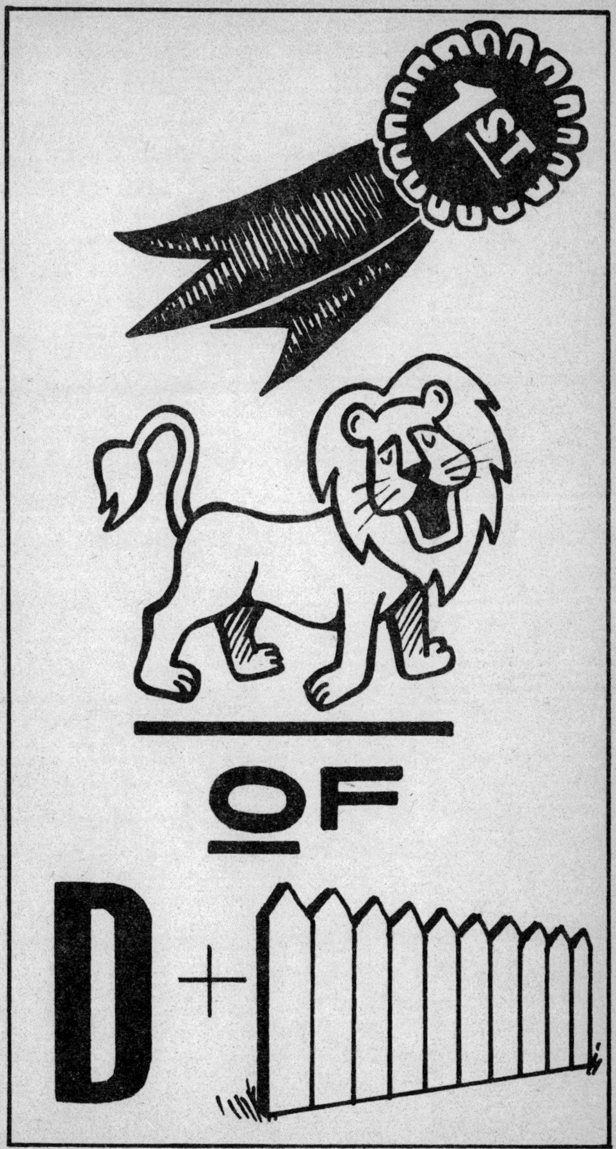
1ST
OF
D
+

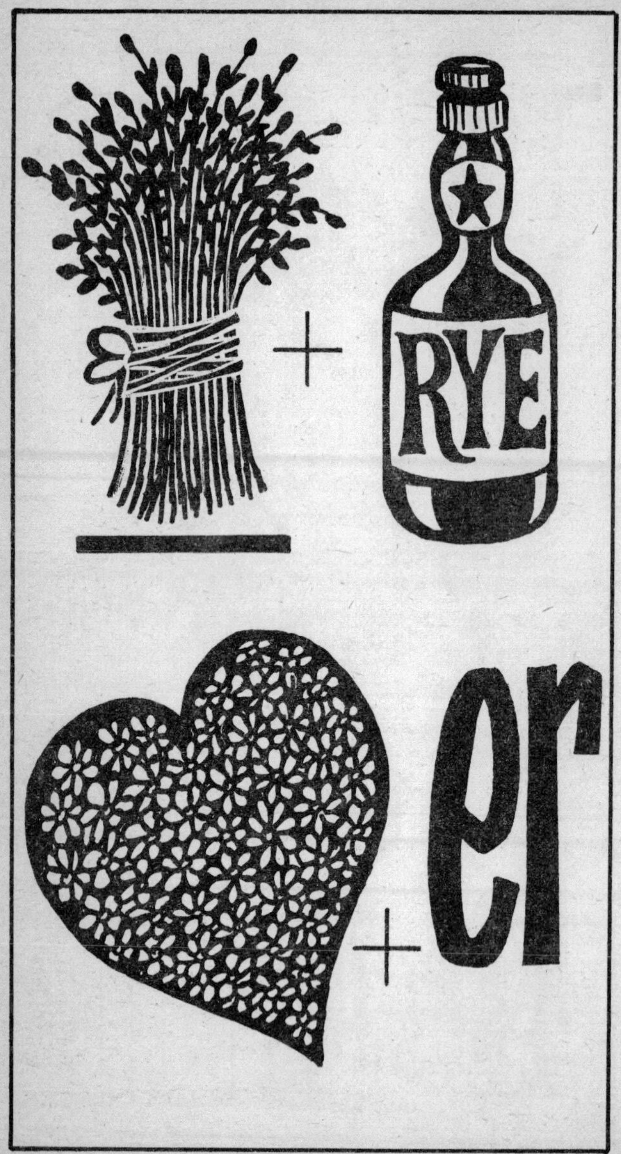
RYE
er

Ip
+
1¢
TH
+
+
HELP
WANTED

88. BARBERSHOP FAVORITE

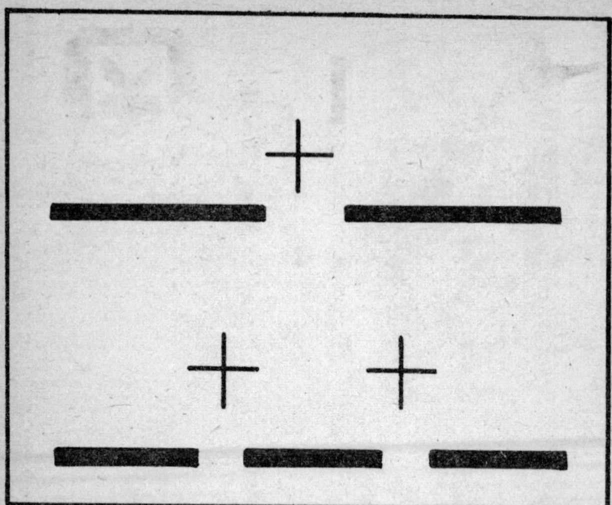

WORK AREA:

"N"
H
hum
INK

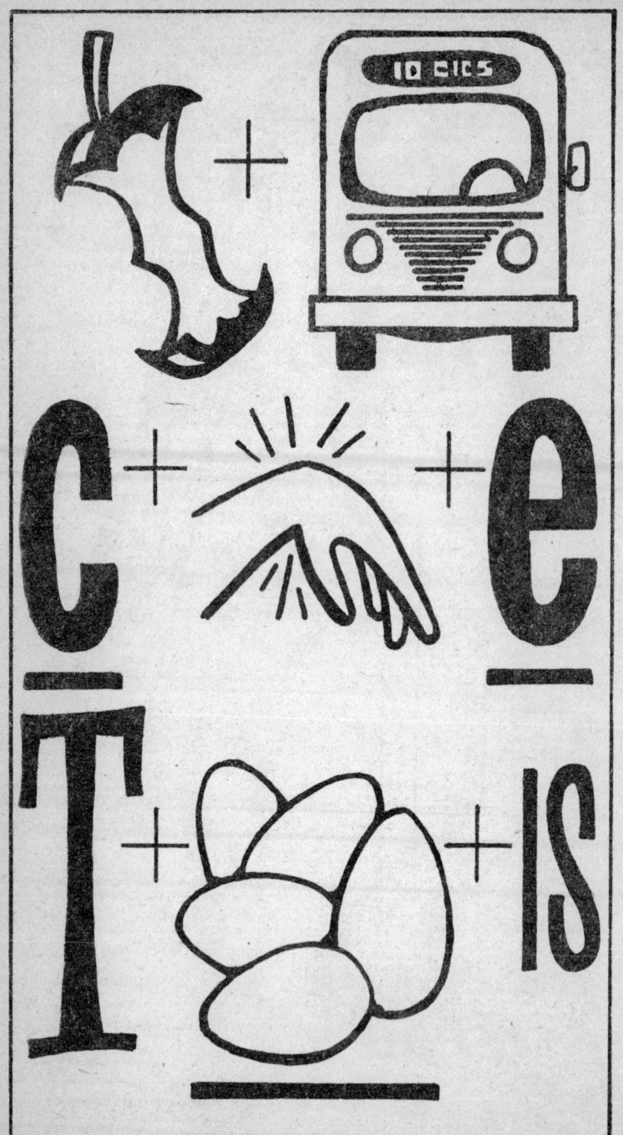
+
c
+
+
e
T
+
+
IS

a
AW

92. PERFECTIONIST

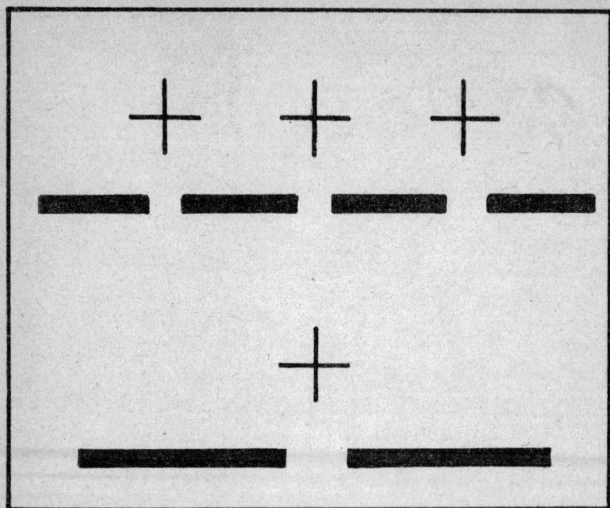

WORK AREA:

YUV
+
m
+

RYE
+ 't
DOWN
THE
+ L

THE
L
&
of
UP
2
E

96. COMICS

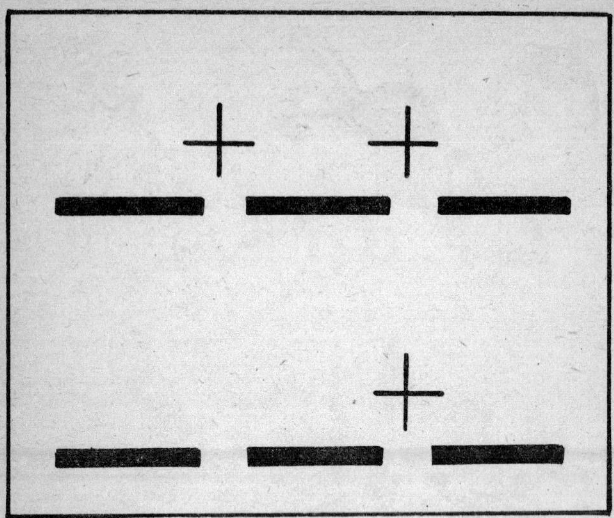

WORK AREA:

S
A
'Z
"o"
i

IS
GOO
'd
40

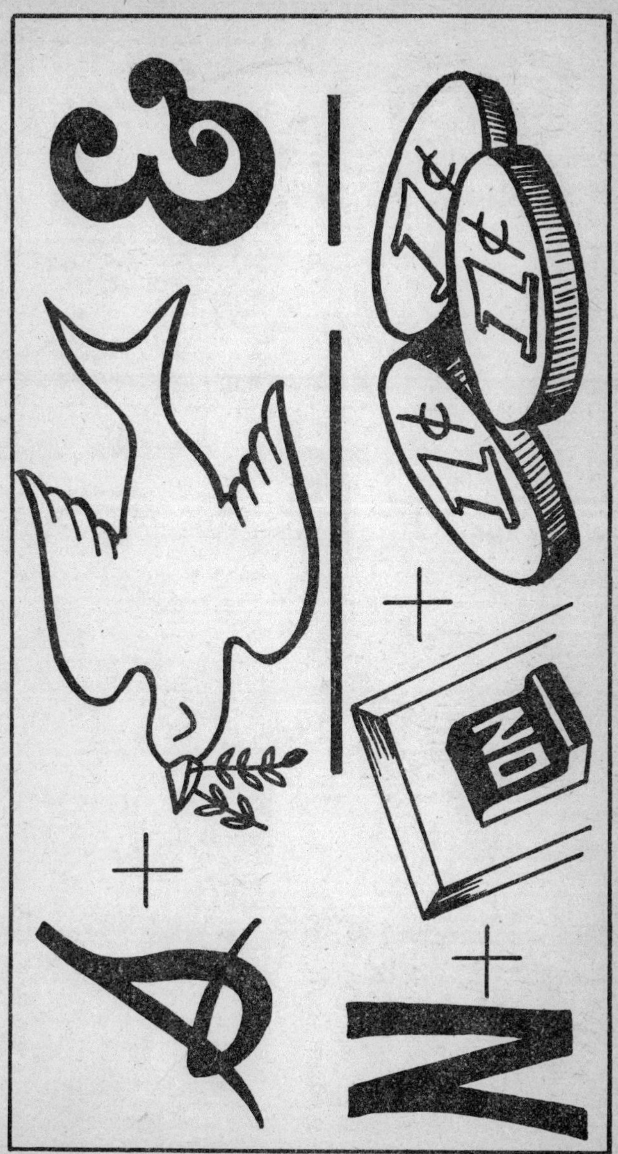
3
A
1¢
1¢
1¢
NO
M

100. BATTLE CRY

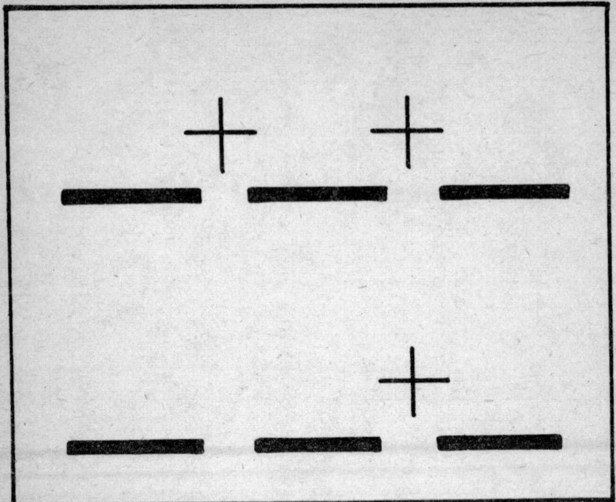

WORK AREA:

YORE
th
WELCOME

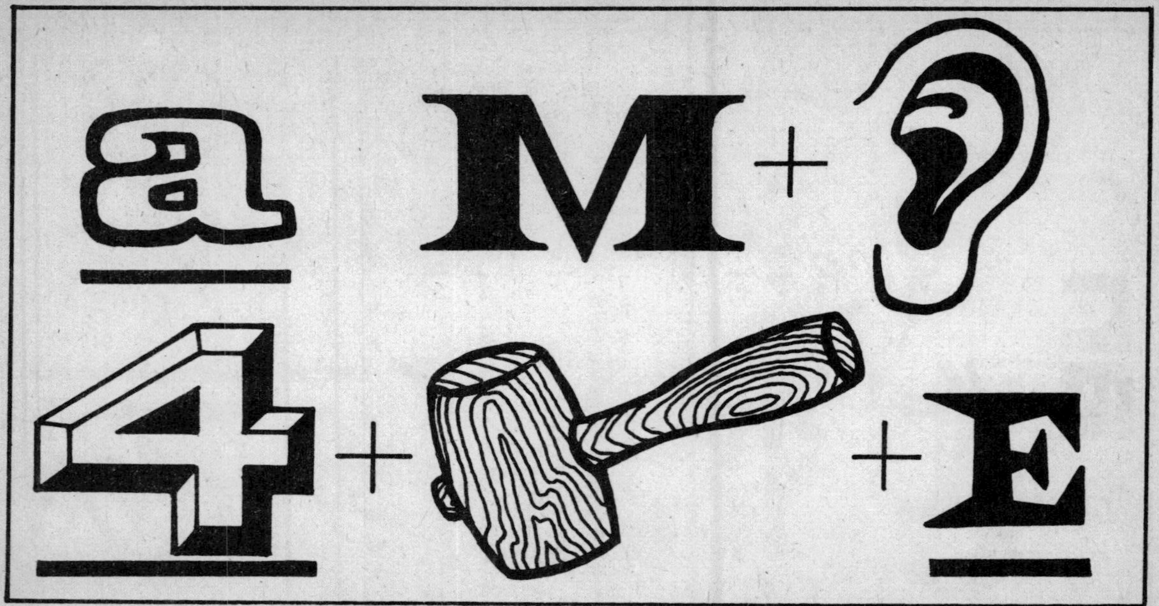
a
M +
4 +
+ E

an
O +
AND
sh +
Cola

104. MONEYMAKING IDEAS

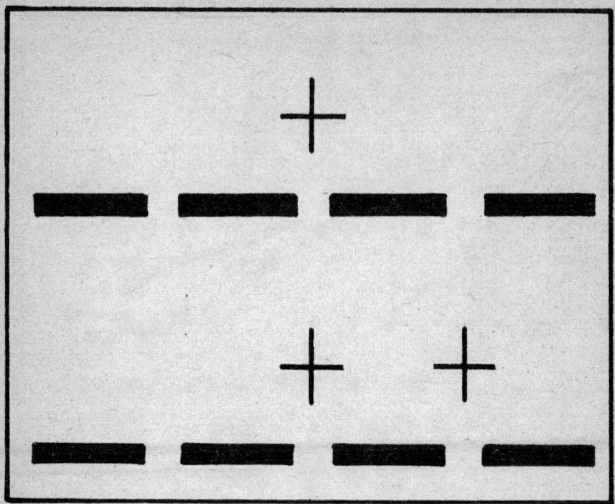

WORK AREA:

'K
un
8

a
F +
W
N
S
E
40

Till
n
+
+

108. SEASIDE SNACK

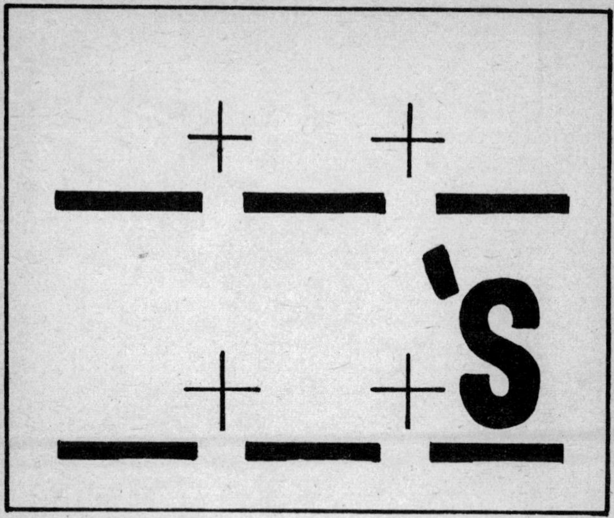

WORK AREA:

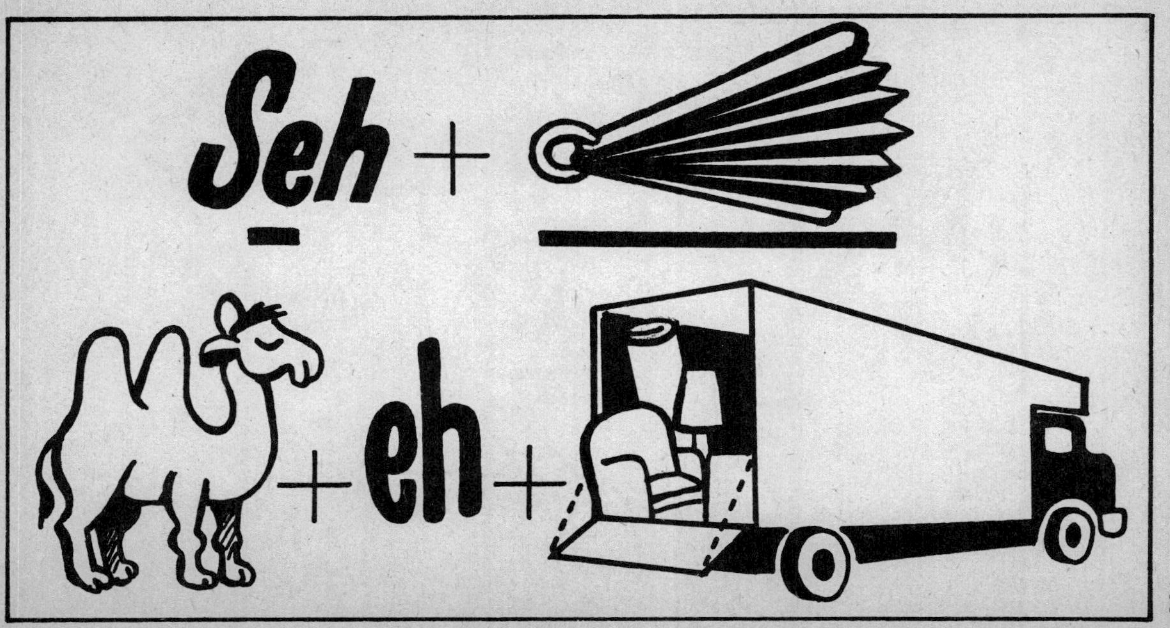
Seh
eh

DOWN
2
m
'R

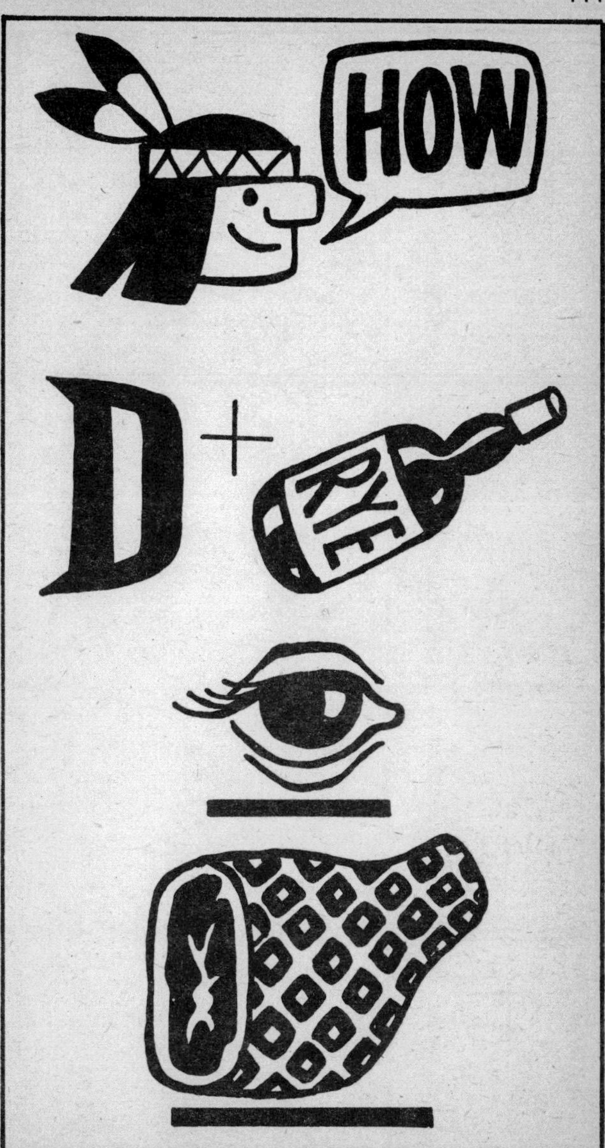
HOW
D
+
RYE

112. TOUGH GUYS

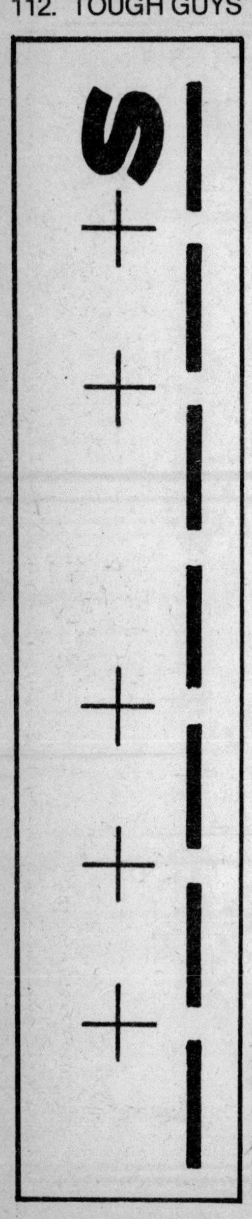

WORK AREA:

LEE
S

P
R
Ting
TOOT
AWK

D
UGH
ING
the
E

116. FINN'S FAVORITE

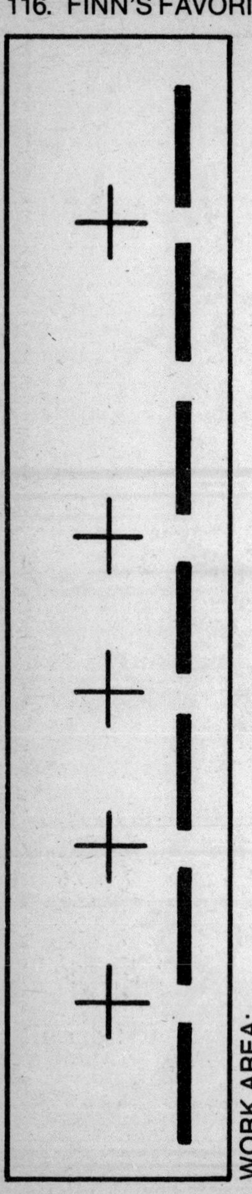

WORK AREA:

N

L + 8
b +
+ ing

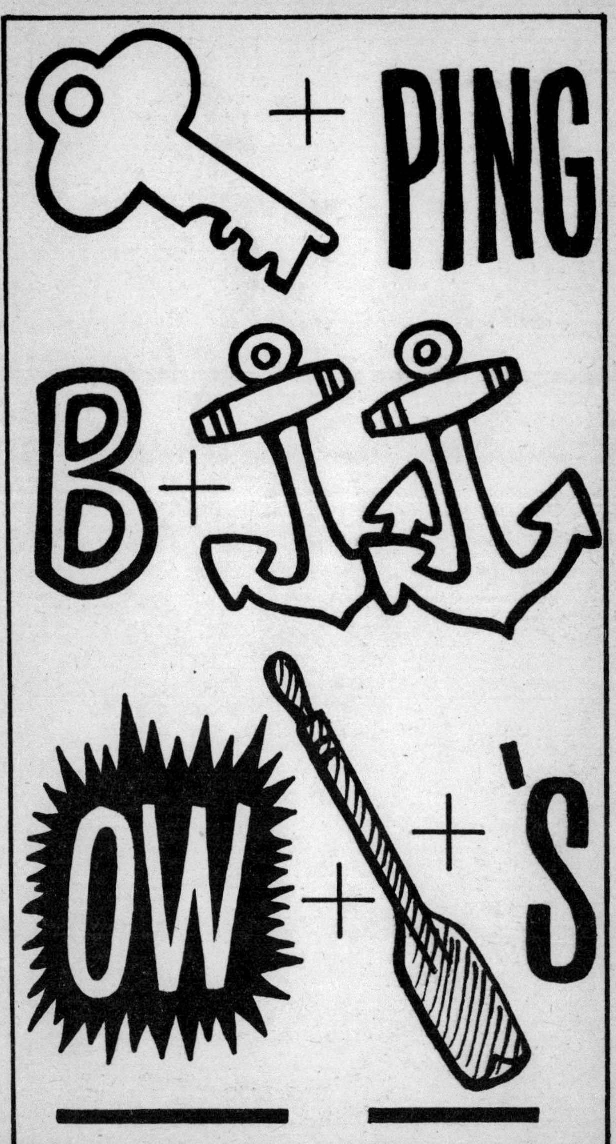
+
PING
B
+
OW
+
+
'S

120. CHARGE IT!

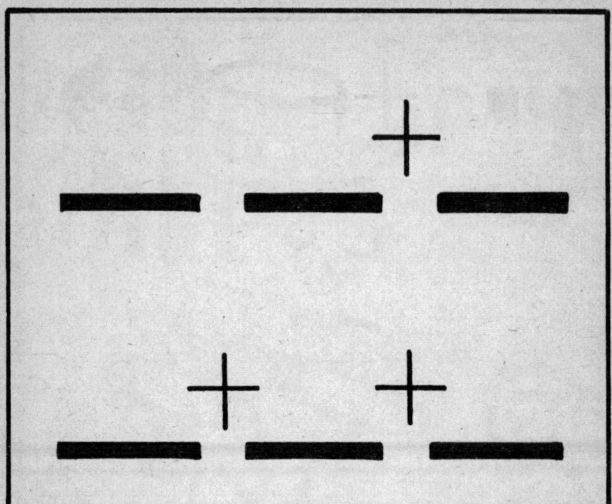

WORK AREA:

TH
+
+
'M
S
+
+
'
T

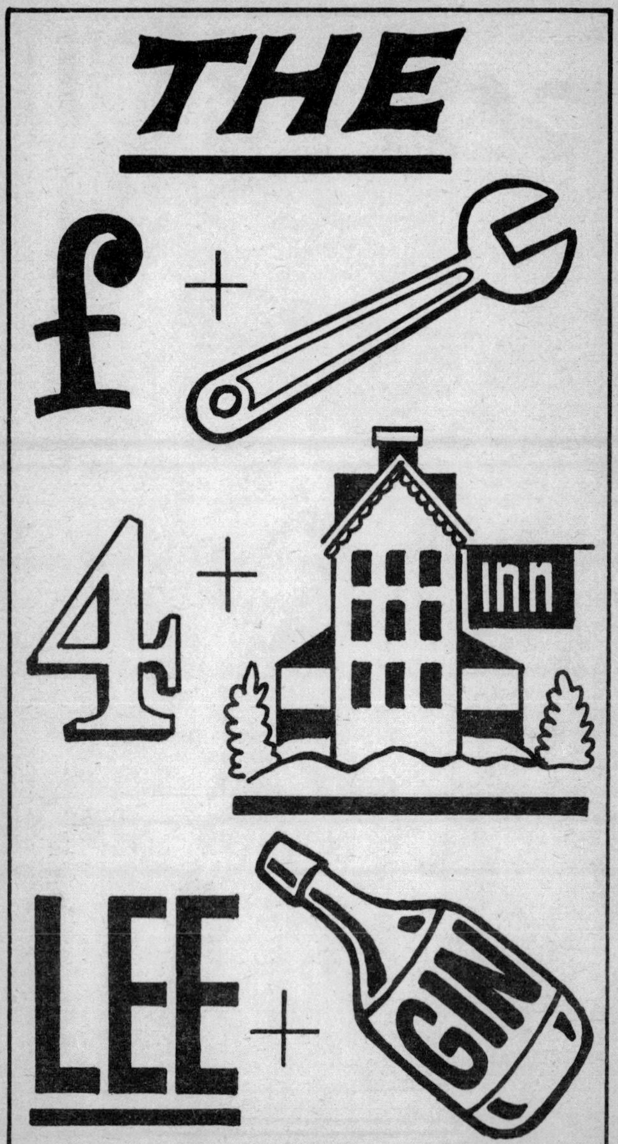
THE
f
+
4
+
Inn
LEE
+
GIN

+ 'D'
IS
no
+ e +

124. THAT'S RICH!

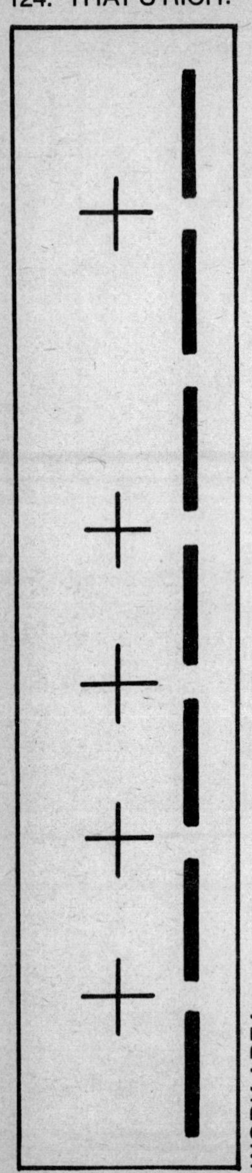

WORK AREA:

TH +
+ U +
N + VIII +

Ch +
UH +
+ 'NT

+
10
THE
+
10¢

128. PLAYWRIGHT

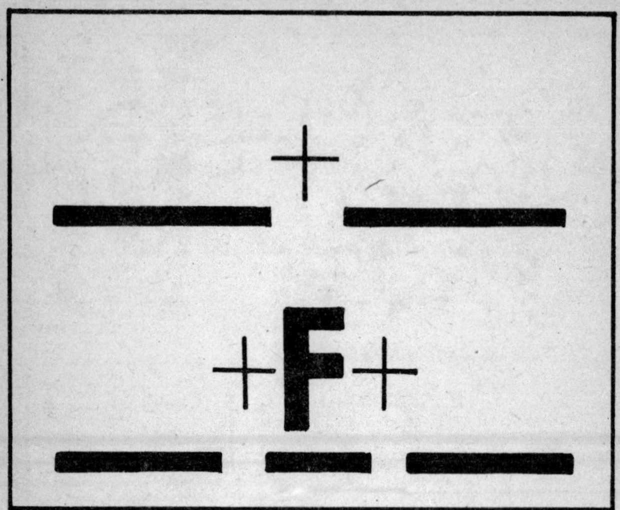

WORK AREA:

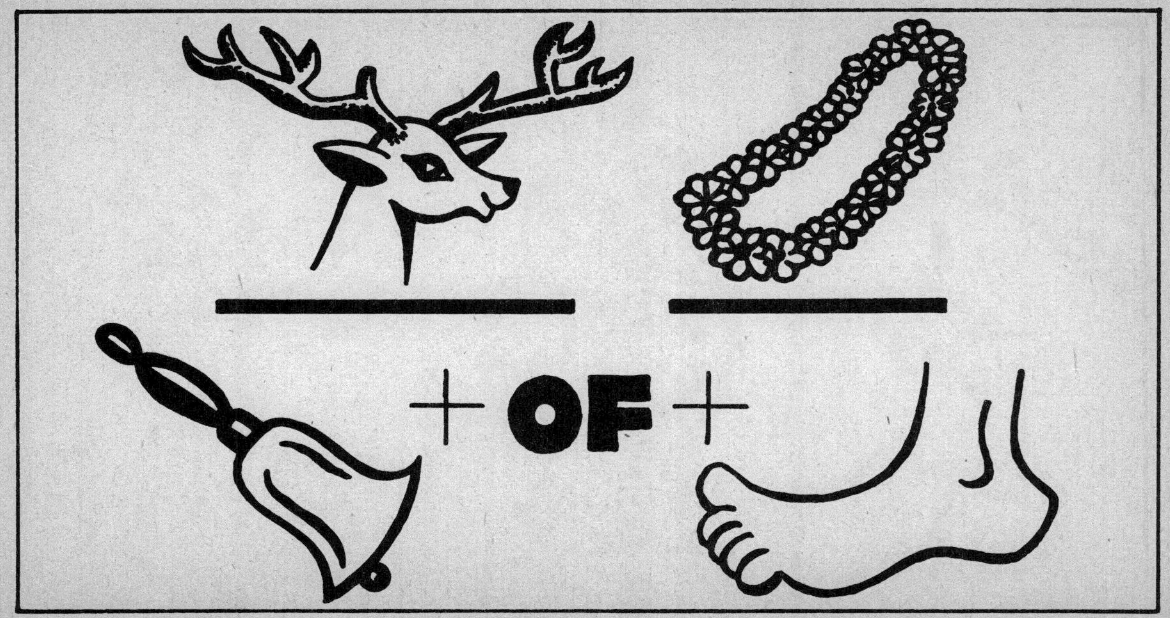
OF

2 Y +
+

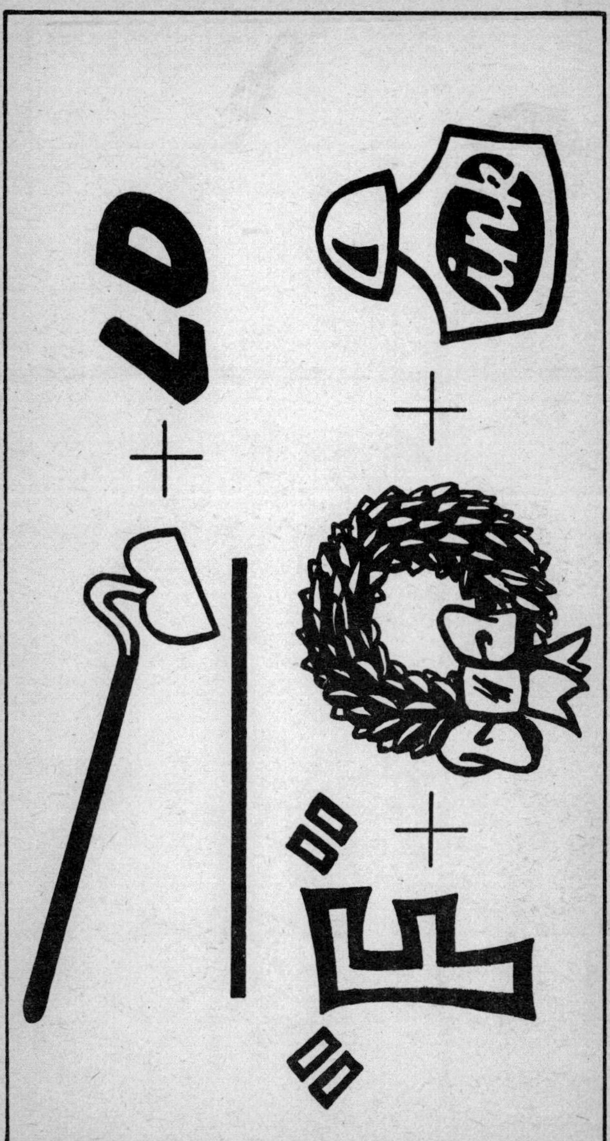

132. BODY OF WATER

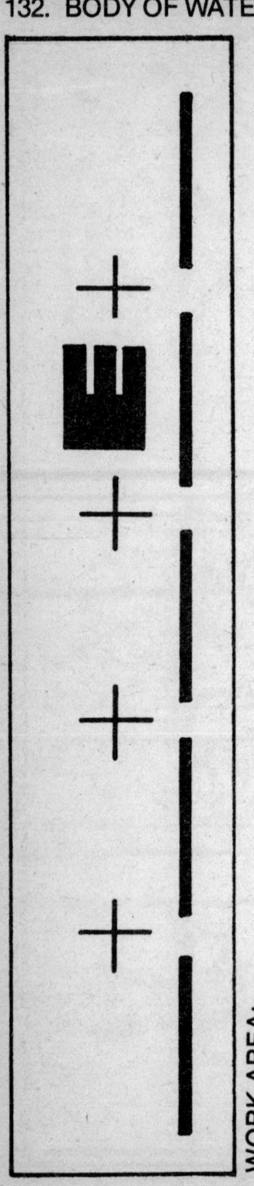

WORK AREA:

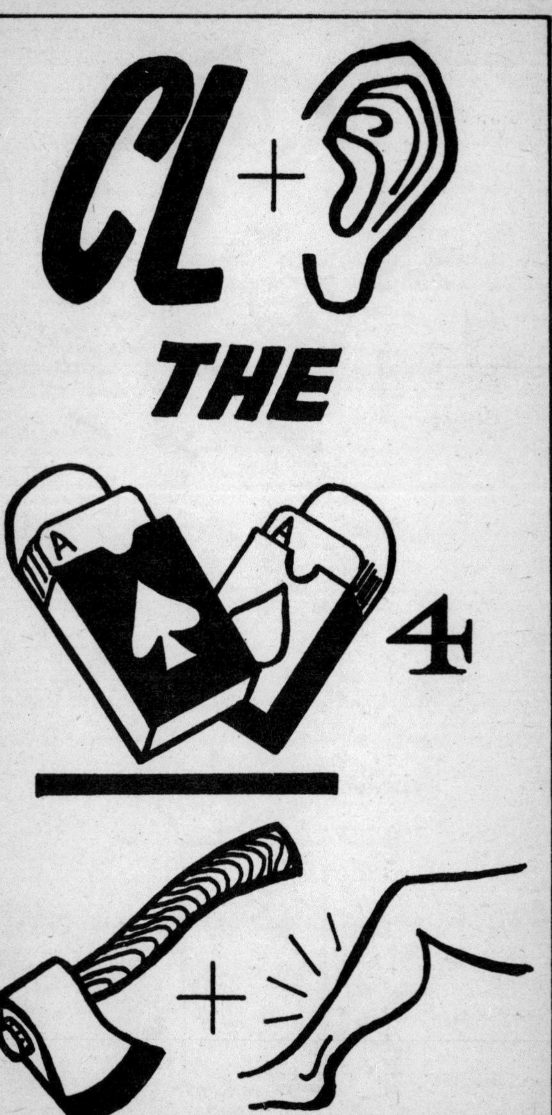
CL +
THE
A
A
4
+

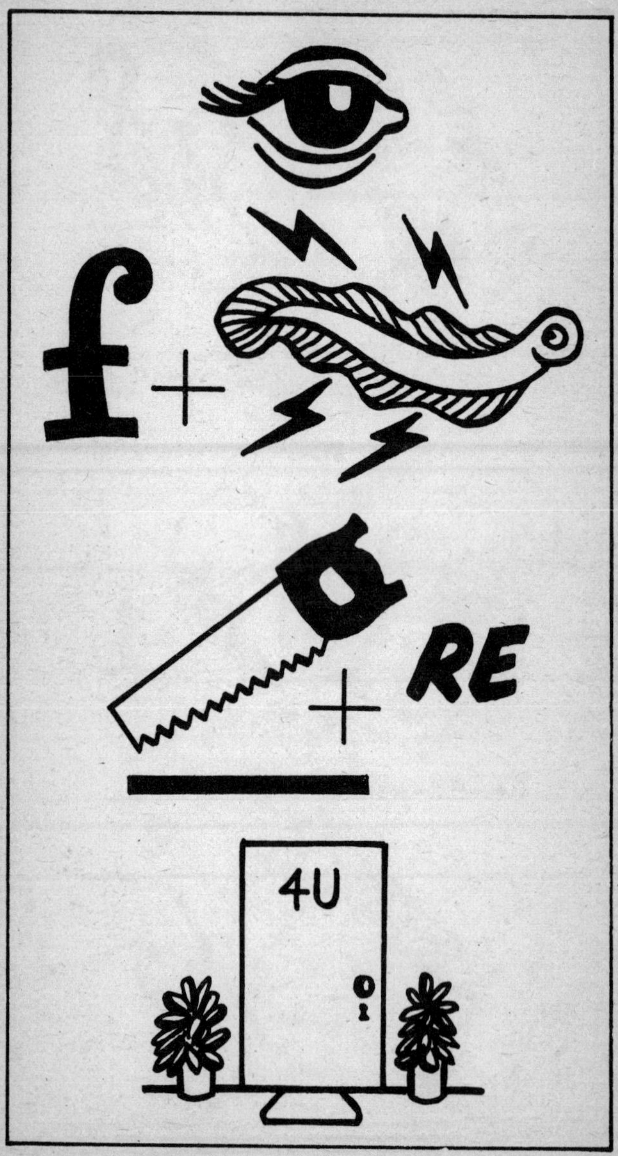
f
RE
4U

The

+
RIGHT

100%
WOOL
+
'F

136. NOT SO HARD

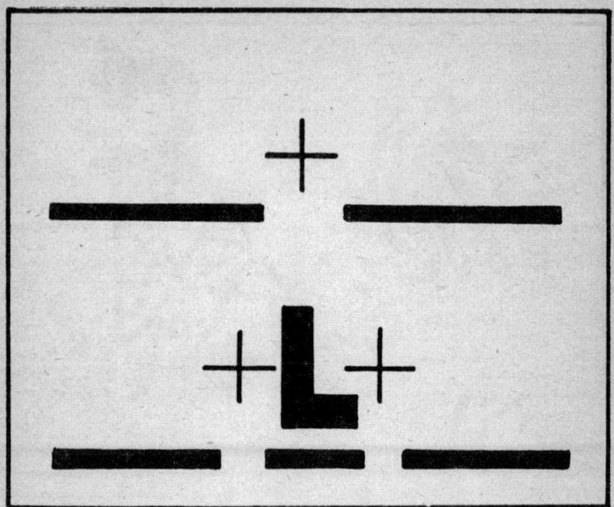

WORK AREA:

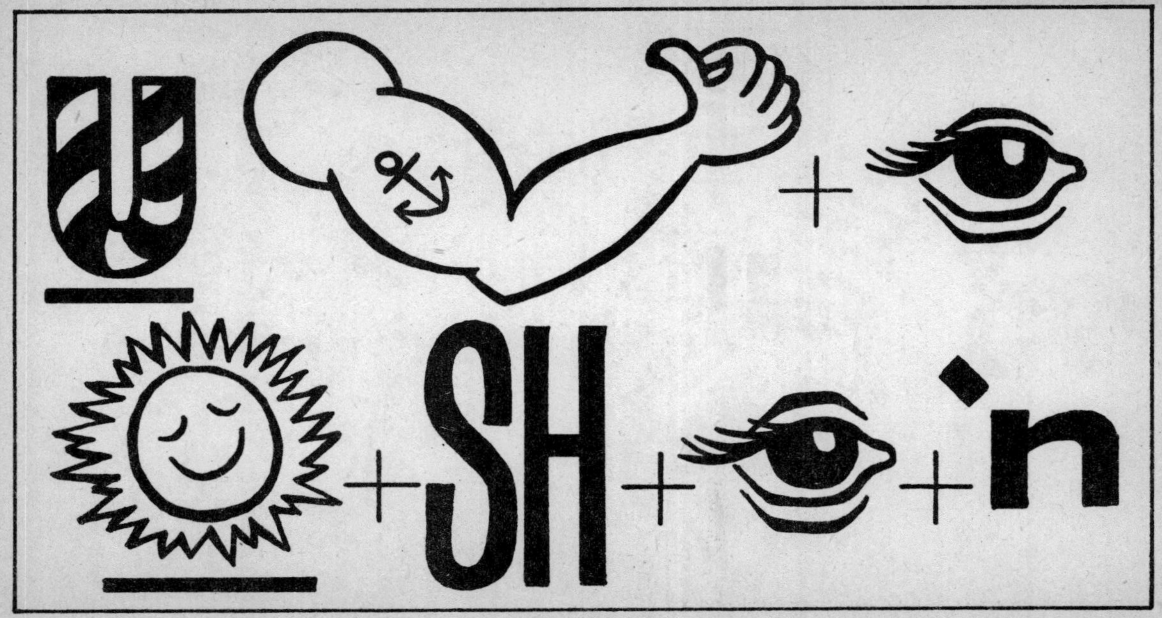
SH
'n

a

+ing

OF the

'

+ds

10¢
10¢
10¢
10¢
'R'
+
Jing

140. JUNGLE LOVERS

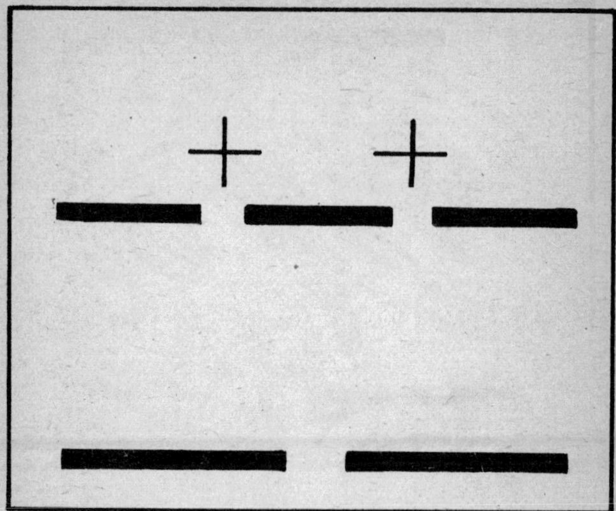

WORK AREA:

ALE
+
+ ding
£ +
+

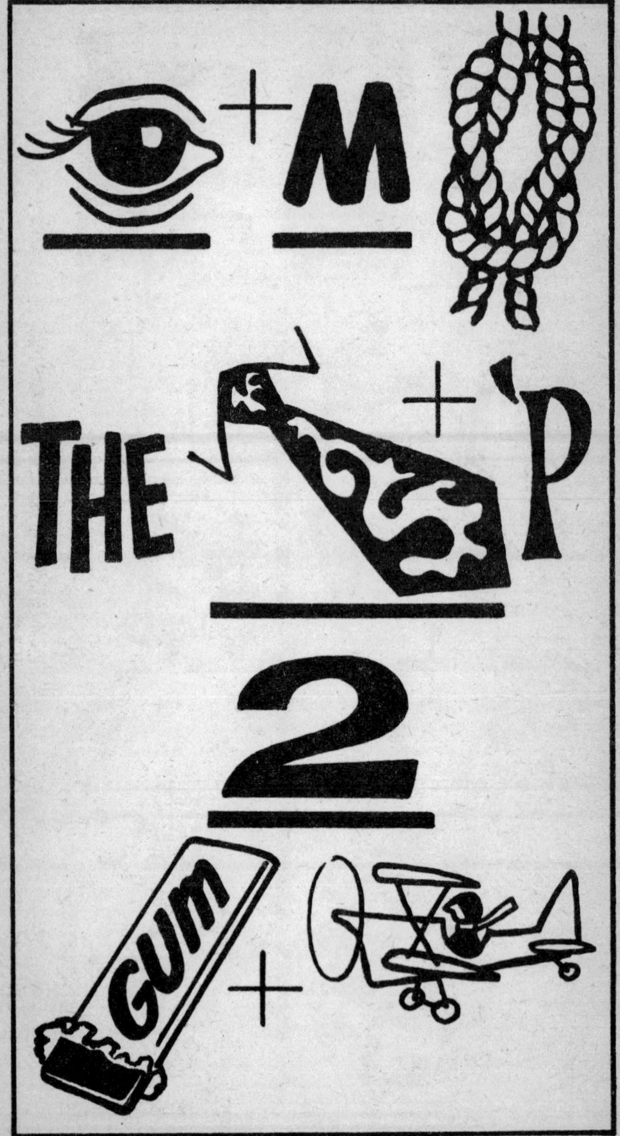
+
M
THE
+
'P
2
GUM
+

A
RUM
+
+
t
pa
+
SOAP
+
+
A.D.

144. UNBREAKABLE

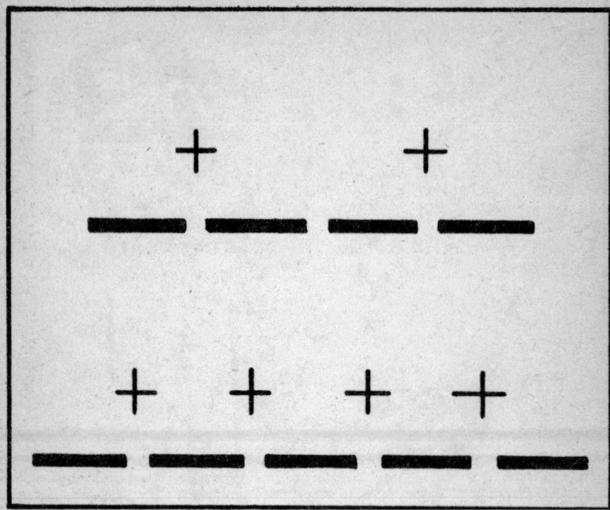

WORK AREA:

its
OW
+
the
K
+
E
S
N
W
+
GIN

THE
P +
Inn
+
5¢
OF
+
Sez

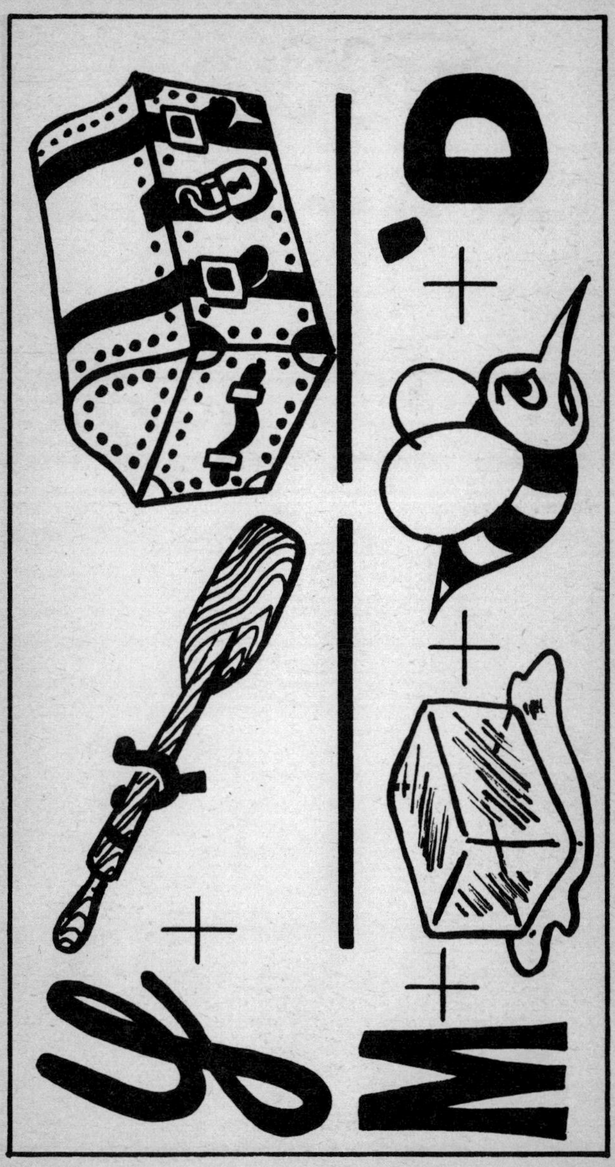

148. HYPNOTIC SPELL

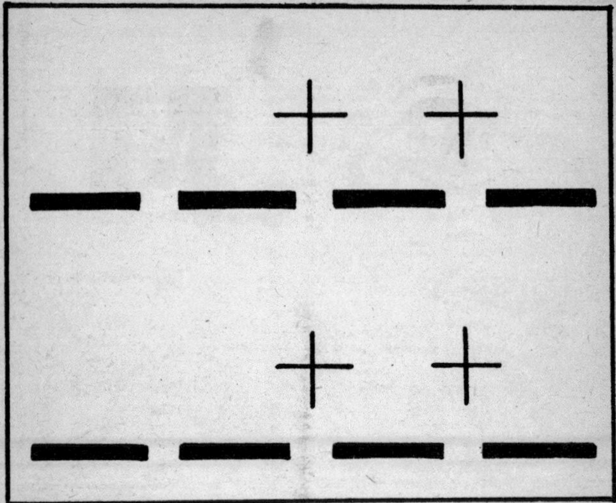

WORK AREA:

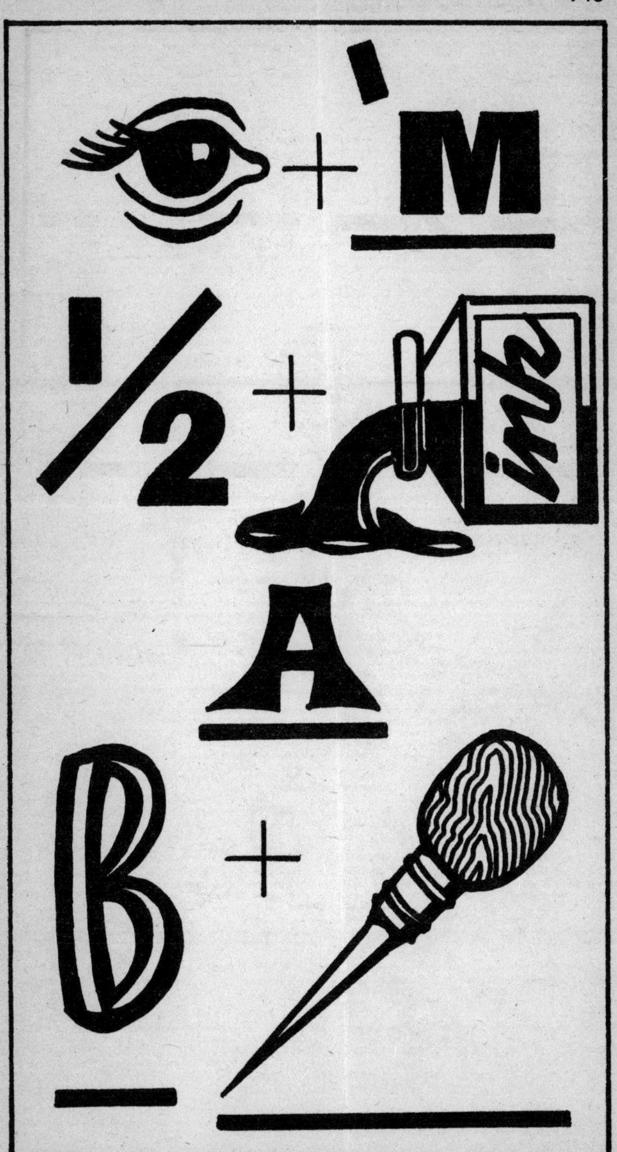
M
1/2
A
B

'U' + RAH!
+ E
GOO
+ 'Z

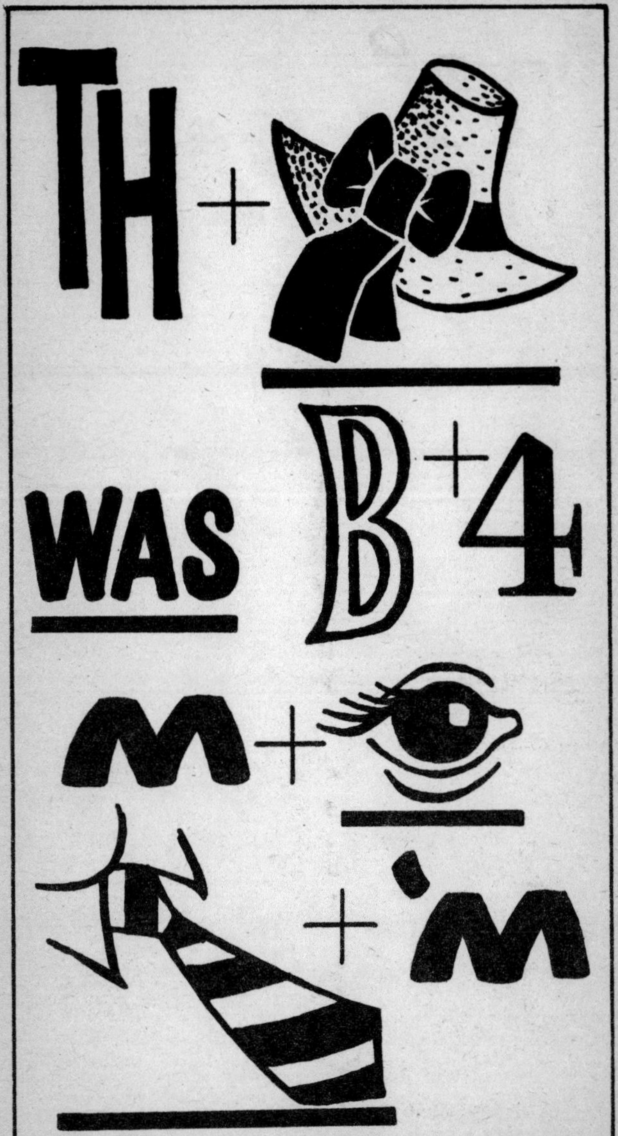

TH +
WAS
B + 4
M +
+ 'M

152. SUCCESSFUL AFFAIR

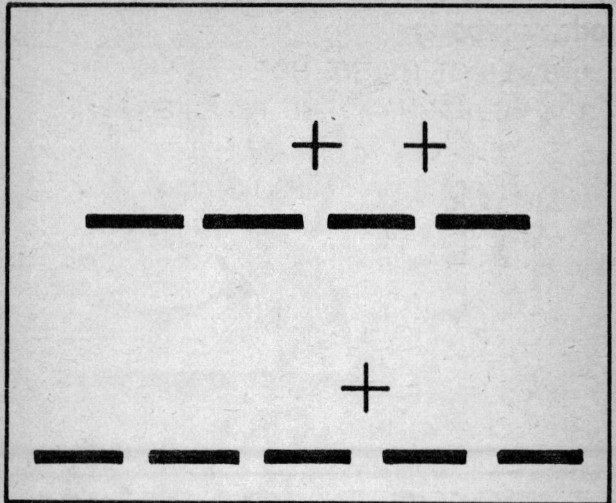

WORK AREA:

SECOND CHANCE SOLUTIONS (odd numbers)

1. HIVE COT H + EYE HOE + 'PS
3. A WELL INN + 4 + 'MD PEAR + SUN
5. F + 8TH + O + PAN CHAIR + 80
7. HOO NOSE WH + AIR OAR WH + HEN
9. DEED U C TH + HAT
11. AN "E" + CORE BEE + 4
13. "C" + CAR S + DOOR INN + "D" + INN
15. FEET + JER 8 + TRACK + SHIN
17. WH + HAIR CHUTE EYE BOOK + IN
19. GLO + WING INN THE D + ARK
21. EYE + 'L S + TRAY + 10
    "F" + WREATH + IN + COW + 'T
23. LOO + SINK A HEART B + RAKE + ER
25. DUH + BALL EGG + 'S + BOWS + YOUR
27. WH + EAR KNOT UH + MOOSE + 'D
29. FULL S + BEE + 'D UH + HEAD
31. GO 2 A NEW + DRILL CORN + ER
33. DOUGH + 'NT F + LYE OFF THE HAND + 'L
35. BOW + AH GUNS + TRICK + DOOR
37. TUBE + E CON + 10 + YOU'D
39. SH + OAR + DOOR + DOOR COO + 'K
41. S + TRAY + 'T TOOTH + E POINT
43. MIKE + GUN + TREE TEA + SAW + 'F THEE
45. DUNCE + BILL THE BEE + 'NS
47. ANNE ERROR IN JUDGE + MINT
49. S + DOOR + M W + AWNING
51. BED + ER U TH + HEN ME
53. RICE 2 THE OK + SHIN

55. AN AP + BALL 4 THE TEA + JAW
57. HOUSE TH + HAT UGH + CANE
59. FILE + INK A COMB + PLANE + 'T
61. THE EAT + URN + L T + RYE + ANKLE
63. K + AIR + "S" F + OIL + 'D A + CANE
65. A MO + KNEE MAY + KING SKI + 'M
67. A TOE + GUN OF M + EYE "S" + TEE + 'M
69. RIT + SHIRT BIRD + TON
71. TRA + BUCKLE PARROT + DICE
73. PAW + TABLE TELLER + FISH + "N"
75. EYE + 'M KNOT A BED + ING MAN
77. TAY + KING TOP AH + NURSE
79. STR + UGH + L 4 SAW + 5 + L
81. SEED + SHOE + A + SHIN KA + MITT + E
83. MOOSE + EGG + LEE INK + LYE + 'ND
85. FIRST LION OF D + FENCE
87. IS + CENT TH + HAT TUBE + AD
89. "N" + GOAL + BIRD HUM + BOARD + INK
91. A STAND + AW + FISH PURSE + HEN
93. YUV CAP + SHIRT M + EYE HEART
95. THE L + & OF UP + OAR + 2 + NET + E
97. S + CORE + RING A BULL + 'Z "I"
99. S + DOVE & N + ON + CENTS
101. YORE AWL TH + HAT MAT + HORSE
103. AN O + PEN AND SH + HUT CASE
105. PIN + 'K LAMB + UN + 8
107. WEIGHT TILL N + EGGS + CHAIR
109. SEH + FAN CAMEL + EH + VAN
111. HOW D + RYE EYE HAM
113. EYE CAN BEAR + LEE S + BEAK

115. D + UGH + ING THE E + SHOE
117. PAIL PIE COMB + ARROWS + N
119. KEY + PING B + ANCHORS OW + OAR + 'S
121. TH + HATS TIE + 'M WELL S + PEN + 'T
123. SAFE + "D" IS NO AXE + E + TENT
125. TH + HATS U + MAN N + 8 + JAW
127. CHESS + 10 THE KNEE + CUFF DIME
129. DEER + LEI BELL + OF + FOOT
131. HOE + LD "F" + WREATH + INK
133. CL + EAR THE DECKS 4 AXE + SHIN
135. THE BUOY HOOK + RIGHT WOOL + 'F
137. U ARM + EYE SUN + SH + EYE + 'N
139. DIMES "R" CHAIN + JING
141. ALE + LASS + DING F + WRENCH + SHIP
143. A RUM + HOE + 'T PA + SOAP + BILL + A.D.
145. ITS OW + DOVE THE K + WEST + GIN
147. Y + OAR CHEST M + ICE + BEE + 'D
149. EYE + 'M 1/2 + INK A B + AWL
151. TH + HAT WAS B + 4 M + EYE TIE + 'M

SECOND CHANCE SOLUTIONS (even numbers)

2. YUV GUM 2 THE RYE + 'T PL + ACE
4. ______ + GUM ______ + ______
6. LEAF WHALE "N" + OFF ALE + OWN
8. ______ + ______ + HEN ______ + ______
10. A PASS + INK FAN + "Z"
12. ______ + ______ ______ ______ BEE ______
14. ON THE SUN + KNEE CIDER THE S + TREE + 'T

16. ______ + ON + ______ ______ + ______

18. B + ALE + UH LOCK + GO + "C"

20. ______ + ______ ______ + EYE ______ ______

22. STAKE + ING A K + LEI + 'M

24. ______ + LEI + ______ A ______ + ______

26. S + DART F + RUM THE TOP

28. ______ + ______ THE ______ + ______

30. YORE WITCH + "S" MIKE + COMB + &

32. ______ + 'D ______ + 'F ______ + ______ + ______

34. 8 + HEN OAK + LOCK S + COLLAR

36. ______ + ______ + DOOR ______ + ______ + ______

38. SW + HORN 2 "C" + GREASE + E

40. ______ + ______ ______ + OAR + ______

42. OAR + L RAH + BIRDS

44. ______ ______ + ______ + GUN ______ + ______

46. A FAN + TAZ + DUCK EYE + DEER

48. ______ + ______ ______ ______ + ERROR + ______

50. TIE + 'T AS A D + RUM

52. ______ + TIE + ______ ______ + ______ + ______

54. ITS PIN ONE OF TH + HOSE D + ACE

56. ______ ______ ______ ______ + ICE ______ ______

58. A + SALT & BAT + TREE

60. ______ + ______ ______

______ + HOUSE + ______

62. KEY + 'P UN + DUCK + UH + 4

64. ______ + DUCK + ______

______ + ______ + ______

66. AN OFF + HAND RUM + ARK

68. ______ + ______ ______ + TOE + ______

70. N + ARROW + WING THE F + EEL + 'D

72. ______ + ______ EEL + ______

74. LYE + 'F CAN BEE BOOT + EVIL

76. ______ ______ + KNOT ______ ______

78. INN A MAN + ER OF S + BEAK + ING

80. ______ + INN + ______ ______ + ______

82. CRAW + 6 + SALMON + ASIAN

84. ______ + LYE + ______ + ______ 2

______ + ______

86. WHEAT + RYE HEART + ER

88. ______ + ______ ______ + O + ______

90. CORE + BUS C + WRIST + E T + EGGS + IS

92. ______ + ______ + HEN + ______

______ + ______

94. RYE + 'T DOWN THE MITT + L

96. ______ + OAR + ______ ______

______ + ______

98. CON + FEZ + SHIN IS GOO + 'D 40 SOLE

100. ______ + EYE + ______ ______

______ + ______

102. A M + EAR 4 + MALLET + E

104. ______ ______ + KNEE ______ YORE

______ + ______ + ______

106. A F + EAST 40 ICE

108. ______ + EAST + ______

______ + ______ + 'S

110. DOWN 2 M + EYE LASS + DOLL + 'R

112. ______ + ______ + ______ + E

______ + ______ + S

114. P + BULL R STAR + TING TOOT + AWK

116. ______ + ______ + L + ______ + E

______ + ______

118. L + 8 B + RAKE + ING NOOSE

120. ______ ______ + ______

PAIL + ______ + ______

122. THE F + WRENCH 4 + INN LEE + GIN

124. ______ + ______ + PEN + ______ + LEE

______ + ______

126. CH + ARCH UH + COW + 'NT

128. ______ + CHESS ______ + F + ______

130. 2 Y + OAR HEARTS CON + TENT

132. ______ + CON + ______ + E + ______

134. EYE F + EEL SAW + RE 4U

136. ______ + 'F ______ + L + ______

138. A MEAT + ING OF THE MINE + 'DS

140. ______ + "R" + ______ ______ ______

142. EYE + 'M KNOT THE TIE + 'P 2 GUM + PLANE

144. ______ + 2 ______ + ______

______ + EYE + ______ + ______ + ______

146. THE P + INN + NICKLE OF SOCK + SEZ

148. ______ ______ + OW + ______ ______

______ + CHEST + ______

150. U + RAH SEAL + E GOO + 'Z

152. ______ ______ + TIE + ______ ______

HAT ______ + ______ ______

SOLUTIONS
(odd numbers)

1. I'VE GOT HIGH HOPES
3. A WELL INFORMED PERSON
5. FAITH, HOPE AND CHARITY
7. WHO KNOWS WHERE OR WHEN
9. DID YOU SEE THAT
11. AN EAGER BEAVER
13. CIGAR STORE INDIAN
15. FEATURE ATTRACTION
17. WHERE SHOULD I BEGIN
19. GLOWING IN THE DARK
21. I'LL STRAIGHTEN EVERYTHING OUT
23. LOSING A HEART BREAKER
25. DOUBLE EXPOSURE
27. WE'RE NOT AMUSED
29. FULL SPEED AHEAD
31. GO TO A NEUTRAL CORNER
33. DON'T FLY OFF THE HANDLE
35. BOA CONSTRICTOR
37. TO BE CONTINUED
39. SHORT ORDER COOK
41. STRAIGHT TO THE POINT

43. MY COUNTRY TIS OF THEE
45. DON'T SPILL THE BEANS
47. AN ERROR IN JUDGMENT
49. STORM WARNING
51. BETTER YOU THAN ME
53. RISE TO THE OCCASION
55. AN APPLE FOR THE TEACHER
57. HOW'S THAT AGAIN
59. FILING A COMPLAINT
61. THE ETERNAL TRIANGLE
63. CURSES, FOILED AGAIN
65. A MONEY MAKING SCHEME
67. A TOKEN OF MY ESTEEM
69. RICHARD BURTON
71. TROPICAL PARADISE
73. PORTABLE TELEVISION
75. I'M NOT A BETTING MAN
77. TAKING TOP HONORS
79. STRUGGLE FOR SURVIVAL
81. SITUATION COMEDY
83. MUSICALLY INCLINED
85. FIRST LINE OF DEFENCE
87. ISN'T THAT TOO BAD
89. ENGLEBERT HUMPERDINCK
91. A STANDOFFISH PERSON
93. YOU'VE CAPTURED MY HEART
95. THE LAND OF OPPORTUNITY
97. SCORING A BULL'S EYE

99. STUFF AND NONSENSE
101. YOU'RE ALL THAT MATTERS
103. AN OPEN AND SHUT CASE
105. PINK LEMONADE
107. WAIT TIL NEXT YEAR
109. SEVEN, COME ELEVEN
111. HOW DRY I AM
113. I CAN BARELY SPEAK
115. DUCKING THE ISSUE
117. PALE BY COMPARISON
119. KEEPING BANKER'S HOURS
121. THAT'S TIME WELL SPENT
123. SAFETY IS NO ACCIDENT
125. THAT'S HUMAN NATURE
127. JUST IN THE NICK OF TIME
129. DEARLY BELOVED
131. HOLD EVERYTHING
133. CLEAR THE DECKS FOR ACTION
135. THE BOY WHO CRIED WOLF
137. YOU ARE MY SUNSHINE
139. TIMES ARE CHANGING
141. A LASTING FRIENDSHIP
143. A REMOTE POSSIBILITY
145. IT'S OUT OF THE QUESTION
147. YOU'RE JUST MY SPEED
149. I'M HAVING A BALL
151. THAT WAS BEFORE MY TIME

SOLUTIONS
(even numbers)

2. YOU'VE COME TO THE RIGHT PLACE
4. WELCOME HOME
6. LEAVE WELL ENOUGH ALONE
8. NATHAN HALE
10. A PASSING FANCY
12. EASY AS A B C
14. ON THE SUNNY SIDE OF THE STREET
16. JOHNNY CARSON
18. BELA LUGOSI
20. GOING BY THE BOOK
22. STAKING A CLAIM
24. BLAZING A TRAIL
26. START FROM THE TOP
28. STOP THE MUSIC
30. YOUR WISH IS MY COMMAND
32. CORNED BEEF SANDWICH
34. A TEN O'CLOCK SCHOLAR
36. BOULDER, COLORADO
38. SWORN TO SECRECY
40. SEAN CONNERY
42. ORAL ROBERTS
44. THE OREGON TRAIL
46. A FANTASTIC IDEA
48. IVAN THE TERRIBLE
50. TIGHT AS A DRUM
52. BEDTIME STORY
54. IT'S BEEN ONE OF THOSE DAYS

56. TWO FOR THE PRICE OF ONE
58. ASSAULT AND BATTERY
60. BATTING A THOUSAND
62. KEEP UNDERCOVER
64. KENTUCKY COLONEL
66. AN OFF-HAND REMARK
68. MARK ANTONY
70. NARROWING THE FIELD
72. ROBERT E. LEE
74. LIFE CAN BE BEAUTIFUL
76. I CANNOT TELL A LIE
78. IN A MANNER OF SPEAKING
80. BEGINNER'S LUCK
82. CROSS EXAMINATION
84. MOST LIKELY TO SUCCEED
86. WE TRY HARDER
88. SWEET ADELINE
90. CORPUS CHRISTI, TEXAS
92. EFFICIENCY EXPERT
94. RIGHT DOWN THE MIDDLE
96. LAUREL AND HARDY
98. CONFESSION IS GOOD FOR THE SOUL
100. DIVIDE AND CONQUER
102. A MERE FORMALITY
104. A PENNY FOR YOUR THOUGHTS
106. A FEAST FOR THE EYES
108. CHERRYSTONE CLAMS
110. DOWN TO MY LAST DOLLAR
112. MIAMI DOLPHINS

114. PEOPLE ARE STARTING TO TALK
116. HUCKLEBERRY PIE
118. LATE BREAKING NEWS
120. BUY NOW, PAY LATER
122. THE FRENCH FOREIGN LEGION
124. INDEPENDENTLY WEALTHY
126. CHARGE ACCOUNT
128. GEORGE S. KAUFMAN
130. TO YOUR HEARTS CONTENT
132. LAKE ONTARIO
134. I FEEL SORRY FOR YOU
136. SOFT BOILED EGGS
138. A MEETING OF THE MINDS
140. ME TARZAN, YOU JANE
142. I'M NOT THE TYPE TO COMPLAIN
144. BUILT TO LAST A LIFETIME
146. THE PINNACLE OF SUCCESS
148. THE POWER OF SUGGESTION
150. YOU'RE A SILLY GOOSE
152. A GOOD TIME WAS HAD BY ALL